Well, That Makes Us Even, Doesn't It?

"We both know you don't trust me."

His words recalled last night and suddenly erected a wall between them that Kit had no idea how to breach. She dragged her gaze away from the dark intensity of his. If only she could have freed herself of all inhibition and thrown herself into his arms, she would have done so in that moment. But the behavior of a lifetime couldn't be eradicated so easily. At last he turned away and she could breathe again, but she had never felt so lost and confused in her life.

DONNA VITEK
firmly believes that "I would probably have never learned to enjoy writing as much as I do" without the helpful influence of her husband, Richard. Silhouette readers will be pleased to know that this is her seventh Silhouette Romance.

Dear Reader:

During the last year, many of you have written to Silhouette telling us what you like best about Silhouette Romances and, more recently, about Silhouette Special Editions. You've also told us what else you'd like to read from Silhouette. With your comments and suggestions in mind, we've developed SILHOUETTE DESIRE.

SILHOUETTE DESIREs will be on sale this June, and each month we'll bring you four new DESIREs written by some of your favorite authors—Stephanie James, Diana Palmer, Rita Clay, Suzanne Simms and many more.

SILHOUETTE DESIREs may not be for everyone, but they are for those readers who want a more sensual, provocative romance. The heroines are slightly older—women who are actively involved in their careers and the world around them. If you want to experience all the excitement, passion and joy of falling in love, then SILHOUETTE DESIRE is for you.

I'd appreciate any thoughts you'd like to share with us on new SILHOUETTE DESIRE, and I invite you to write to us at the address below:

Karen Solem
Editor-in-Chief
Silhouette Books
P.O. Box 769
New York, N.Y. 10019

DONNA VITEK
Game of Chance

Silhouette *Romance*

Published by Silhouette Books New York

America's Publisher of Contemporary Romance

For Mabel Welfare
and
Janet Rothrock

SILHOUETTE BOOKS, a Simon & Schuster Division of
GULF & WESTERN CORPORATION
1230 Avenue of the Americas, New York, N.Y. 10020

ISBN: 0-671-57157-5

First Silhouette Books printing June, 1982

10 9 8 7 6 5 4 3 2 1

America's Publisher of Contemporary Romance

Printed in the U.S.A.

Chapter One

.... *The tall dark man held out a bronze hand to Katherine and the confident glint in his warm blue eyes conveyed an unmistakable warning. Her heart fluttering madly against her breastbone, Katherine gazed up at him and understanding his silent command, placed her smaller, ivory hand in his, trembling as he drew her to him. A powerful arm encircled her slender waist as he brushed a kiss against the thickness of her auburn hair. "Katherine, don't be afraid, I'll always take care of you," he murmured, his voice deep and persuasively melodious. One lean finger lifted her small chin. He lowered his dark head, smiling triumphantly as the soft curves of her body melted against the long hard line of his. Then his sensuously carved mouth covered hers and . . .*

"Are you going to Tahoe on vacation?" the girl in the seat next to Katherine's asked, interrupting the divine fantasy. "Or do you work there?"

With a silent regretful sigh, Katherine Delacorte dragged herself back to reality and turned away from the plane window. Tucking a wayward wisp of gold-streaked auburn hair behind her ear, she gave the petite brunette beside her a friendly smile, despite the fact that she really would have preferred to remain lost in her daydream rather than indulge in idle chitchat with a stranger. Besides, she and the girl were the two youngest passengers on this flight to Lake Tahoe so Katherine supposed that did give the brunette and her something in common. Smoothing the skirt of her sand-colored suit, Katherine answered the inquiry. "I don't work there, but I'm not really on vacation either," she said softly, a hint of shyness in her voice and her emerald green eyes. "I'm going to spend the summer with my father."

The brunette's perfectly arched brows lifted. "Ooh, he must be loaded if he can afford to spend a whole summer in Tahoe."

Smiling indulgently, Katherine shook her head. "Actually, he lives there."

"Oh, wow, really?" the brunette exclaimed, unduly impressed. "What's his name? Is he *somebody?*"

"I imagine he thinks he is," Katherine answered wryly. "And I know that he's my father, at least. But I don't suppose that's exactly what you meant, is it?"

The other girl giggled. "Not exactly. I meant is he anybody famous?"

"Not that I know of. He just happens to live near Lake Tahoe because he runs a casino at one of the hotels."

"Not Harrah's?" the brunette squealed, attracting the attention of most of the other passengers. "Ooh, do say that's where he works! *Please!* It would be just so fabulous for me to know someone who knows someone who works at Harrah's. My name is Wendi Miller and I'm a singer and I'd just absolutely die of happiness if I could get a

8

chance to sing in one of the lounges at a famous hotel like that."

Katherine grimaced apologetically. "Sorry to disappoint you but my father doesn't work there. He runs the casino in a much smaller hotel—Cedars."

"Oh, but I've heard of that, too," Wendi informed her, gesturing excitedly. "Cedars is a pretty exclusive little place, isn't it? I think most of the big names in show biz have played there at one time or another so I wouldn't mind singing in one of the lounges there either."

Katherine smiled politely. "How long have you been singing professionally?"

"Five years. Since I was twenty." Wendi laughed humorlessly. "But you wouldn't believe some of the dives I've had to work in. You know, the kind of places where the customers are so stoned they wouldn't care if you were yodeling. It hasn't been a lot of fun, I can tell you."

"Then why do you keep doing it?"

A bitter little smile hardened Wendi's features. "I'm twenty-five and all I've ever done is sing. I wouldn't know what else to do if I quit now. Besides, I know if I could just get a little lucky, I could really make it big and that's what I'm aiming for. I'd do *anything* to be a superstar."

"I hope you make it then," Katherine said sincerely, feeling oddly more mature at age twenty-one than Wendi was at twenty-five. And she knew she was definitely more realistic. "I hope you don't mind me saying this, but don't you think it's a bit risky to come to Tahoe just on the hopes of getting work at one of the lounges? Wouldn't it have been better to let your agent arrange a booking?"

"My agent! Ha! That's a laugh," Wendi snapped with a derisive snort. "That worthless son of a . . . Well, never mind what he is. Just let me say that he's the reason I've been singing in dives for the past five years. So last week, I finally decided to dump him. I'll find my own bookings now and will probably do a better job of it than he ever did. As I said, I'd be willing to do anything to get just one big break."

Not doubting that for a moment, Katherine nodded. "I wish you good luck, then, if singing means that much to you."

"I need more than just luck, though," Wendi said, leaning closer to Katherine and eyeing her speculatively. "If only I knew someone at one of the hotels, someone like your father, who could introduce me to the right people. Why, he might even know the person who books the entertainment at Harrah's and of course, he knows whoever does it at Cedars. He's exactly the kind of connection I need," she added suggestively.

Katherine refused to take the hint, though she realized her father wouldn't mind if she chose to introduce Wendi to him. In fact, he might enjoy it and as Katherine recalled all the other young women like Wendi she had seen him with over the years, her dread of the coming summer at Tahoe rushed back from the recesses of her mind where she had managed to push it with her daydreams. She sighed inwardly. Every year it was like this. While her mother, stepfather, and half-sister and brothers spent the summer together in Baltimore, she was shipped here to Nevada to spend two and a half long months with a man she hardly knew and one for whom she felt little real respect, despite the fact that he was her father. This year she had tried her best to escape coming. It had been worth it to her to sign up for both summer semesters at college to avoid the trip but even that little ploy hadn't succeeded. Since Brice Delacorte footed the bill for her college education, he had informed her he wouldn't pay the tuition for summer school because he wanted her to spend the two and a half months with him, as usual.

Katherine had never figured out why he was so eager to have her with him every year. In all the summers since she was four years old, he had never paid very much attention to her. While she stayed in his house in the hills above Lake Tahoe, she had received more affection from his long-suffering housekeeper, Mallie, than she had ever received from him. It was a mystery to her why he hadn't simply forgotten all about her after deserting her mother and her when she was only three. She almost wished he had. Then her stepfather could have adopted her and she would have really felt a part of her mother's second family all these years instead of seeing herself as something of an outsider. But Brice had never been willing to relinquish his claim on her and, to his credit, he had always helped support her financially, if in no other discernible way.

He was an irrepressible gambler and a lovable rogue. Katherine's mother could now say this without any bitterness but Katherine couldn't find it in her heart to be so magnanimous. Though she supposed she loved her father, she neither liked nor respected his lifestyle. And she wasn't about to introduce him to Wendi so the two of them could use each other for a few weeks, then forget each other existed.

Ignoring Wendi's expectant stare, Katherine turned away to gaze down at the wisps of fluffy white clouds through which the plane was now descending. Suddenly, the cloud band dissipated and as the plane turned in its approach to the airfield, the view below made Katherine's eyes widen in appreciation as it had never failed to do. At least her father didn't manage a casino in Las Vegas or Reno, she thought wryly, gazing in awe at the panoramic view of Lake Tahoe. Much as she hated to come here on general principle, she had to admit it had to be one of the most beautiful places in the world. The dark sapphire lake was nestled in a basin of the Sierra Nevada mountains right on the Nevada-California border.

Pine and cedar forests covered the slopes surrounding the jewel-clear waters and cottages and hotels with finger-like piers perched on the rocky shoreline. As always, Katherine tried to imagine how exquisite it would be in Tahoe in the winter with snow covering the ski terrain that was now, in early June, acre after acre of green meadowland sprinkled with yellow and white wildflowers. Snow-covered and in the frosty-clean mountain air, she knew it had to be beautiful and sometimes she wished her father would ask her to spend a Christmas here instead of expecting her to spend the whole summer every year with him.

The landing went smoothly and soon Katherine was in the terminal waiting for her luggage. But just as she saw her two blue suitcases start around on the wide conveyor belt, Wendi Miller claimed her attention.

"Well, I'm off to find myself the cheapest hotel room around," the older girl said too cheerily. "Then, I suppose I'll just have to start making the rounds, trying to get someone to book me in one of the lounges. It would be nice though if I just knew somebody here," she added expectantly and when Katherine only ignored the obvious hint again, she shrugged. "I just wanted to say good-bye."

Katherine smiled, feeling a certain pity for the girl though not enough to set her up with her father. "It was nice talking to you," she said politely instead. "I hope you get lucky and find a job right away."

"Well, I'll certainly try my best to see that I do," Wendi said, her voice taking on a hard edge. There was something almost manipulative in her eyes when she gave Katherine a half-smile. "What's your name anyway? When we talked on the plane, I told you mine, but you never told me yours."

Obligingly, Katherine introduced herself.

"Well, see you around, Kathy Delacorte," Wendi said airily, tossing up a small hand weighted down with at least one ring on every finger. "Maybe I'll just show up at

Cedars one day soon and see how you're doing. Bye-bye now."

As the older girl strolled off across the terminal, her hips swaying provocatively, Katherine smiled slightly to herself, knowing Wendi had only wanted to know her name because of her father. If she did come to find her at Cedars, it wouldn't be to renew their slight acquaintance. She would come hoping to meet and impress Brice Delacorte so that he might use whatever influence he had to get her booked in a lounge in one of the hotels.

With a soft resigned sigh, Katherine turned back to the ever-moving belt and waited for her luggage to come around again. After retrieving her two suitcases, she hurried away to catch the courtesy bus that would take her to Cedars. There were several other passengers besides Katherine but she managed to find a seat to herself left of the aisle where she could sit by the window, though the scenery during the first part of the ride didn't exactly thrill her. As soon as the highway crossed the state line into Nevada, the casinos cropped up and since Katherine had never gambled in her life nor did she plan to, these establishments caused her no excitement. Neither did the lake's south shore with its high-rise hotels, those concrete-and-glass monoliths, which in her opinion marred the natural alpine beauty surrounding them. Yet, she sat by the window because she knew what came after the main highway was left behind. A narrow secondary road wound its way north along the lake through virgin stands of pine and cedar, overlooking the clear azure waters glimmering in the mid-afternoon sunlight. As if she were seeing the lake and the snow capped Sierras towering above it for the first time, Katherine gazed out her window, enthralled by the bewitching loveliness. When the bus turned off the narrow winding road onto a cedar-lined drive that de-scended down to the shore, however, Katherine heaved a

13

regretful sigh. Even the sight of the gracious old Cedars Hotel bordered by the vibrant green grass of the nine-hole golf course didn't lift her spirits. Though the sprawling, cream-colored wooden building with its wide wrap-around verandas and second- and third-story balconies created an impression of pristine charm on the exterior, the interior was not so aesthetically lovely.

Without enthusiasm, Katherine left the bus, collected her luggage and went inside, wishing as always that the entrance foyer decorated with lush red carpet, gold-embossed wallpaper and heavy, dark furniture wasn't marred by the inevitable slot machines that lined the walls. Even in mid-afternoon, nearly every machine was being played and Katherine tried not to notice some of the avaricious expressions so evident on some of the players' faces as she made her way to the long mahogany registration desk. The clerk in attendance was a stranger to her, but when she informed him she was Brice Delacorte's daughter, he was happy to take her luggage for safekeeping.

With a resolute stiffening of her shoulders she crossed the small, quiet lobby and entered the vast noisy confines of the casino. She wrinkled her nose unconsciously at the smoke-filled air. To the sound of clinking ice in innumerable glasses, she threaded her way between the green baize-topped keno, blackjack, and baccarat tables, taking care not to be trod on by any of the chattering gamblers who thronged around them. At the carved mahogany door of her father's office suite, she paused a moment, her hand on the ornate brass knob as she looked back across the casino, a perplexed expression flitting across her delicate features. What in the world could be so fascinating in watching a small ball spin round and round on a roulette wheel? She simply couldn't understand gambling's appeal.

In the gold-carpeted outer office, the receptionist behind a chrome and hardwood desk was new to Katherine, too, but once again the name Delacorte gained her speedy access to the private secretary's office.

"No, don't buzz Jess," Katherine whispered conspiratorially to the receptionist. Gently turning the brass doorknob, she raised a silencing finger to her lips as she softly added, "I want to surprise her."

Jess Whitney, Brice's secretary for the past ten years, didn't look up from the papers on her teakwood desk as Katherine quietly opened the door and stepped into the richly paneled office with plush ivory carpet and kelly green velvet drapes pulled open at the wide windows. For a moment, Katherine stared silently at the only woman who had shared any kind of lasting personal relationship with her father since he had ended his marriage. And to Katherine's dismay, the first thought that came to her mind was that Jess was far too good for him. In her late thirties, with shoulder-length strawberry blonde hair and a slender, youthful figure, she was attractive, yet there was something more than mere prettiness in her face. She had character and warmth, which she displayed immediately when she glanced up and found Katherine hovering in the doorway.

"Kit, we didn't know exactly what day to expect you," she said softly, though a gleam of excitement shone in her dark brown eyes. She stood and hurried from behind her desk to give Katherine a light hug and a genuinely affectionate kiss. "It's so good to see you, though I'm surprised I recognized you with your lovely long hair all done up on your nape that way. I mean, you look beautiful but older than you did last year."

"I decided it was time to change my image," Katherine said wryly, smiling up at the taller woman. "I was tired of looking like I was thirteen."

"Well, you've succeeded. Now you look at least sixteen," Jess said, smiling teasingly when Katherine wrinkled her nose. "No, really, you've become a beautiful young woman. Brice is going to be so surprised when he sees how much you've matured since last year."

Katherine's smile faded slightly. She doubted her father would have noticed if she had arrived in Tahoe in diapers, shaking a baby rattle. But she didn't even attempt to express that opinion to Jess, who would only insist that it wasn't true. For such an intelligent woman, she was pathetically blind to Brice's weaknesses and Katherine could only hope she would never be that unrealistically in love with any man. She wished Jess weren't either, even if it was her own father whom the woman loved. Jess was one of those genuinely good people who deserved all the best life had to offer—a secure existence, a couple of children, and a husband who loved and appreciated her for what she was. She would never find that sort of safe, sane life with Brice Delacorte and no one knew that better than Katherine.

"I thought maybe you wouldn't be here when I came this summer, Jess," she murmured compulsively, her usual shyness overpowered by her concern for her father's secretary. "In fact, I was almost hoping you wouldn't be, for your sake."

A nearly tangible veil of self-protecting aloofness settled over Jess Whitney's pleasant features as she attempted to say laughingly, "I never knew you were eager to be rid of me, Kit. I thought you liked me."

"It's because I like you that I wish you would go away," Katherine said softly, urgently. "And you know why I feel that way. You deserve a much nicer, fuller life than you have here."

"I don't recall complaining about my life," Jess answered stiffly, her tone as aloof as her expression. "I'm happy enough, I assure you."

"You can't expect me to believe that, Jess," Katherine said gently, shaking her head. "I know you're in love with my father and have been since you came to work for him when you were twenty-eight. I even know you had a brief affair with him, that you thought he was in love with you too, and that when he started seeing someone else, you still loved him too much to leave and try to forget him. Mallie told me all about it last summer when I was here and . . ."

"Mallie has a big mouth, then," Jess said grimly, stiffening her shoulders. "She shouldn't have told you anything about Brice and me. What happened between us was a long time ago and all but forgotten. She shouldn't have dredged up the past and upset you by making it sound as if Brice did me some terrible wrong. He didn't, you know. I was an adult. I knew what I was doing when I got involved with him. So, please, forget what Mallie told you. There's no need for you to worry about me."

"But I do!" Katherine exclaimed softly. "I hate to see you wasting yourself on a man like him. You're so nice, Jess, and it's not too late for you to find someone else, someone worthy of . . ."

"Since when did you get your license to give advice to the lovelorn?" Jess interrupted rather sharply, then relented with an endearing grimace. "I'm sorry I snapped at you, but really, I'd rather not discuss this anymore, if you don't mind."

"But, Jess, why waste your whole life on a man like my father?" Katherine persisted. "He's never going to change. And, much as you obviously still love him, I don't see how you've endured the past ten years, watching him indulge in affair after affair with other women. How have you been able to stand it?"

Jess gave a smile that was too weary and too wise. "You've never been in love, have you, Kit?" she asked softly. "Well, after you've found the man you know you'll love all your life, ask yourself how I've endured it. I think you'll begin to understand. Love isn't something you can just turn off like a water faucet. It's tenacious. And it can survive all kinds of hell. I know that much from experience and don't think I haven't tried to stop loving Brice because I have."

"Maybe you haven't tried hard enough." Katherine laid an imploring hand on the other woman's arm. "If you left here . . ."

"I could never leave Brice, Kit," Jess said softly, sadly. "He needs me. Really. Even if you don't believe that and even if he doesn't even realize he needs me, he does. Your father is not as shallow as you think he is. He has emotions; he just doesn't know how to go about showing them. I could never walk out on him. It simply isn't that easy to do when someone needs you. But you'll discover that when you fall in love."

"Ha! I hope I never do then," Katherine muttered disgustedly. "And if I do, it'll never be with a man like my father who always takes and never gives anything back in return. I want to fall in love with a man who can give me some emotional security along with his love. And if I can't find someone like that, then I'll just never fall in love at all."

Smiling ruefully, Jess shook her head. "You're so young, Kit. You don't know yet that we can't always choose the right person to fall in love with. Sometimes it just happens."

"Well, it's not going to just happen to me," Katherine declared with typically youthful false assurance. "I'll never fall in love with any man like my father." She sniffed disdainfully. "He may charm some people, but to me he's an irresponsible . . . "Her words halted abruptly as the man she was describing in such uncomplimentary terms suddenly opened his office door. Overwhelmed with shyness again, Katherine felt herself shrinking inside as she stared at him. He hadn't noticed her yet; the statuesque blonde with him was claiming all his attention at the moment. Another in his long, endless string of casual affairs, Katherine was sure, and she glanced out of the corner of her eye at Jess, who seemed to be resigned to the situation and too accustomed to Brice's indiscretions to even be upset.

At last Brice Delacorte glanced up and saw Katherine. As he disentangled himself from the blonde's clinging bare arm, one of those reluctant, uncomfortable smiles lifted one corner of his mouth. He walked across the office to her, leaned down, and brushed a barely discernible kiss against the slight hollow beneath one high cheekbone. "I'm glad to see you made it here safely, Kit," he said unemotionally. "Did you have a pleasant flight?"

Katherine nodded, noticing at this close range that the lines around his mouth had deepened since last year. For all of that, he was still a handsome man with green eyes and chestnut hair graying at the temples. She had to admit to herself that women would find him very attractive and might even be challenged by his cool, self-controlled demeanor.

"Doesn't Kit look lovely, Brice?" Jess prompted when the silence between father and daughter lengthened uncomfortably. "She's beginning to look more her age than she did last year, don't you think?"

"You look great, Kit," he answered, still expressionless. Then he turned to his blond companion, waving her toward the door. "Better get to rehearsal, hadn't you? I think you need it. You were out of step often enough in last night's revue."

"But Brice," the blonde whined petulantly, "aren't you going to introduce me to your daughter?"

"Later maybe," was his noncommittal answer. "Right now you need to rehearse more than you need an introduction to anybody. So go. You don't want to get fired, do you?"

The blonde went but with an indignant toss of her tawny mane of hair, to which Brice paid absolutely no attention.

When she had closed the office door behind her, he stood for a moment, stroking his chin thoughtfully. Looking at Katherine finally, he gave another one of those crooked, uncomfortable smiles. "Are you in any hurry to get to the house, Kit? If not, I want you to take some drinks back to some of the boys. Two of our cocktail waitresses aren't in today so we're a little shorthanded. You don't mind, do you?"

Katherine breathed a silent sigh. She minded, not that it would do her the least bit of good. Last summer she had been drafted for waitress duty on two occasions and she was sure it would have happened more often if she hadn't avoided coming to the casino as much as possible. Now, she hadn't been here more than ten minutes and already she had been drafted again. She supposed she could stand it though. At least she didn't have to wear one of those skimpy uniforms the regular cocktail waitresses wore.

When she nodded finally in reluctant agreement, Brice said flatly, "You look like a schoolmarm in that suit. At least take off the jacket. Then go out to the bar and tell them you want the drinks for the private game."

"How's it going back there anyway?" Jess asked as she settled herself in her swivel chair behind her desk again. "They've been playing all night, haven't they? When's it going to end?"

"Soon," Brice said sardonically. "I don't think our young heir to a fortune in oil fields is so sure he wants to become a professional gambler now. Jason is practically cleaning him out."

How exciting, Katherine thought disgustedly as she left the office, jacketless, and went to the bar to pick up a tray with four drinks on it. As she walked down an opulently decorated hall beyond her father's office, she wondered why he had cared what she wore to serve these men. It wouldn't have mattered if she'd gone in dressed in sackcloth and ashes or even wearing nothing at all, actually. She hadn't ever seen a professional gambler yet who noticed anything but the hand he held when he was in a hot game.

Unsurprisingly, none of the five men around the table in the private room even looked up as she opened the door and went in. But she eyed them disdainfully. Expensive ties loosened, collars unbuttoned, hair ruffled, they all looked the same to her except . . . Well, she had to admit the sandy-haired man in his early thirties at the far side of the table did look a little more presentable than the rest of them. It was easy to recognize that the younger man on his right was the heir to the oil fortune. He was perspiring profusely, obviously an amateur who had fancied himself a professional gambler and had gotten in over his head. He looked quite miserable, almost sick as he wrote out an I.O.U. and handed it to the sandy-haired man who took it without an iota of change in the unreadable expression on his lean, tanned face.

Gamblers, Katherine thought, wrinkling her nose impatiently as she approached the table with the drinks. Gamblers were men who were hard and cold and totally devoid of emotion and that made them nearly worthless human beings, in her opinion. As she quietly asked each one in turn which drink he'd ordered, they all stared at the poker hands they held as if they were wondrous works of art. Not one of them so much as thanked her and as the oil fortune heir snatched his bourbon and water off the tray without giving her half a chance to hand it to him, Brice Delacorte came into the room.

"I see you found them, Kit. Very good," he said quietly. "I just remembered I forgot to mention which private room the game was in."

Katherine half-smiled at him and then, though she was fairly eager to escape the smoke-filled room, she realized she had only served four drinks and there were five players here. Since she was standing beside the sandy-haired man, she leaned over him.

"Excuse me, sir, but I wasn't given anything for you," she said softly, politely. "Wouldn't you care for a drink?" As he lifted his head lazily, she detected the slight stubble of a day's growth of beard on his strong chin but it wasn't his need of a shave that disturbed her. It was the appreciative gleam that shone in his steel-blue eyes as they traveled appraisingly over the length of her slender body, then lingered intently on her mouth. When she blushed, he actually smiled at her, something she had never seen a gambler involved in a game do.

"I think I'll just have coffee," he said at last, his voice deep and melodious. "Thank you, Kit."

Her cheeks grew hotter. "My name is Katherine," she muttered defensively. "I prefer being called that."

"I prefer calling you Kit. It suits you better," he answered with an unabashed grin. "Now, how about that coffee, Kit?"

"Be my guest," she whispered irritably. "The coffee urn's on the table directly behind you."

As the man's eyebrows lifted mockingly, Brice interceded. "For heaven's sake, Kit, pour Jason a cup of coffee," he muttered impatiently. Can't you see he's in the middle of a game here?"

A game he was obviously going to win, Katherine thought with a disgruntled sigh as she obediently poured a cup of coffee. Even though she had never played poker, she knew enough about it to realize that the three aces Jason held virtually assured he would win.

"Thank you, Kit," he murmured, a hint of amusement in his deep voice as she put the cup of coffee down on the table next to his elbow. "I hope I didn't cause you too much trouble."

Without bothering to answer, Kit collected the tray and

marched to the door but before opening it, she was compelled to glance back over her shoulder. Heat suffused her cheeks once more as she found Jason watching her intently, that appreciative gleam in his blue eyes again. Pressing her lips firmly together, she lifted her chin, opened the door, and left. But outside in the corridor, she paused, frowning as she realized that except for the light hair, this enigmatic Jason looked very much like the man in her recurring daydream. Far more disturbed by that realization than she cared to admit, she walked on slowly. Then she resolutely shook her head. What did it matter if this Jason might be a danger to some susceptible, vulnerable females? That had nothing whatsoever to do with her. She would probably never see him again anyway and even if she did, it would make no difference. She had decided long ago never to become involved with a gambler and that certainly included him.

Chapter Two

In Brice's white Porsche, an off-duty croupier from the casino drove Katherine from Cedars to her father's house about an eighth of a mile along the narrow, winding road. Secluded in a stand of tall stately pines, the wood-frame lodgelike dwelling faced the lake and the property extended down a shaded path to a charming cove enclosed by jagged rock formations. To Katherine's delight there was a short stretch of beach where she invariably spent most of each summer, swimming in the cold, bracing water or simply sitting on the warm sand, daydreaming. Or, when she tired of those occupations, she hiked along the trails that meandered over the slopes rising above the opposite side of the secondary road. Though she never wanted to come to Tahoe, she had to admit she found pleasure and some serenity in the majestic splendor of the Sierras. She supposed if she had to unwillingly spend two and a half months a year somewhere, this was the best place to be. And even here, it could have been worse. Her father could have resided at the hotel and she could have been spending every summer in that resort atmosphere without even the privacy and peace she found here in this house tucked away in the woods.

After the blackjack dealer had left her luggage on the sundeck and had driven away again, Katherine stood at the railing and gazed with some longing at the path that led down to the cove and its beach. If she didn't dillydally, she decided, she would have time for a leisurely swim before she would need to begin getting ready for dinner. Picking up one suitcase, she turned and knocked on the front door. When there was no response from inside the house for several minutes, Katherine simply opened the door and went in. She saw immediately that her father had redecorated his living room. Now, the pieces of a white sectional sofa were arranged in a cozy grouping facing the stone fireplace. There were several chrome and glass tables bearing pieces of smooth, modern, abstract sculpture and modern paintings that seemed to her little more than vivid splashes of vibrant colors on canvas decorating the white plaster walls.

Wondering what had been done to the room she used, she decided finally that there was only one way to find out and she called out to Mallie. There was a sudden clatter of pans in the kitchen that was situated behind the far end of the living room. Then a plump woman in her fifties with a beaming smile on her face opened the louvered doors and hurried to Katherine.

"Miss Kit! Ain't you a sight for sore eyes?" she exclaimed, enfolding the slender girl in a near smothering hug against her ample bosom. Then she held Katherine away from her slightly, her perceptive blue eyes sweeping over her in a close, intense inspection. "Child, if you ain't turned into a real beauty and grown up too in the past year."

"Oh, I haven't changed all that much, surely. Not since

last summer," Katherine said modestly. "I just look different, maybe a little older because I'm wearing my hair up now."

"And I like it thataway, too." Mallie shook her head approvingly. "I'm glad you didn't let nobody cut all that pretty hair off shorter than some boys are wearing theirs these days. Craziest thing I've ever seen—girls with shorter hair than boys'. It's a good thing you didn't have yours shorn off that way. I'd have turned you over my knee if you had."

Katherine didn't doubt that for a minute. In her much younger days, she had occasionally felt the housekeeper's hand meting out punishment on her fanny, especially when she had disobeyed and wandered away from the house where Mallie no longer could see her playing safely. A mountain woman, Mallie wasn't especially talkative but when she did speak, she said exactly what was on her mind and when she made threats, she carried them out. Yet, there was never any doubt in Katherine's mind that Mallie loved her and her tender affection made up in some degree for her father's indifference.

Compulsively, Katherine hugged Mallie again briefly and brushed another kiss against her plump cheek, then sighed. "Well, tell me how you've been this winter. I worried about you when you never answered my letters. What was wrong? Arthritis in your hands again?"

"Some mornings they was so stiff I could hardly move 'em, especially during the coldest spells. But," Mallie added sheepishly, "I never was much for writing letters anyhow. But it sure pleased me to hear from you. Now, I bet you're wanting a bath after your trip so let's get you settled in your room. While you're soaking in the tub, I'll do the unpacking for you."

Agreeing with that suggestion eagerly, Katherine retrieved her second suitcase from the deck, then followed Mallie down a long corridor that led to the bedrooms at the back of the house. Though her father had redecorated her room with plush white carpet on the floor and forest green-sprigged muslin drapes and bedspread, he hadn't replaced the cedarwood furniture she loved. All of it was still there, the bed with its carved head and footboards, the chest of drawers, and carved vanity, and the old hope chest that she had always hidden her most precious belongings in as a child.

She rummaged through a suitcase, found her favorite faded denim bikini and went into the adjoining bathroom, closing the door behind her and hurriedly peeling off her clothes. After a cool shower, she felt considerably fresher and more energetic and she was smiling as she stepped out of the marble tiled shower stall onto a plush white bathmat. But as she wrapped a huge towel around her slim body, her smile faded abruptly. Hanging on the back of the bathroom door was a nearly transparent black night-gown and it certainly wasn't Katherine's. Her lips pressed firmly together, she wriggled herself into her bikini, snatched the nightgown off the brass hook, and opened the door to her room.

She tossed the provocative garment toward her bed and it drifted like a wisp of smoke before Mallie's startled eyes, then settled in a heap on the bedspread. "Unless you've taken to wearing frothy nightgowns," Katherine said stiffly, "this must belong to one of my father's *'friends.'*"

A rosy blush crept into Mallie's cheeks. "I meant to get that thing outa there before you got here. I'm sorry, child."

"No need for you to be sorry," Katherine said with a toss of her head. "I know my father brings women here."

Mallie gestured helplessly. "Now, mind you, I'm not saying I approve of his loose ways but he is a man, Kit, and men need . . . er . . . female companionship now and again. It's only natural."

"And I suppose it's natural for men to flit from one

woman to another, like a bee moves from flower to flower?" Katherine asked, unable to disguise her disgust. "Well, that's really charming."

Mallie twisted her plump, gnarled hands in front of her. "Kit," she began gently, "your father is a lonely man."

"Is he?" Katherine countered disbelievingly, flopping down onto the vanity seat. "I don't think he is. I think he's just shallow. He's quite content to satisfy his purely physical needs with these one-night stands of his. If he wanted something more, he could get it from Jess Whitney. But he doesn't want love. He doesn't even know what the word means."

"Your daddy loves you, Kit," Mallie declared softly. "So I reckon he knows what the word means."

Katherine shook her head obstinately. "I don't think he even loves me. Her certainly doesn't show it."

"Some folks can't show how they feel. Your daddy's like that, but he loves you. Why else do you reckon he has you visit him every summer?"

"Guilty conscience, maybe," Katherine answered with a careless shrug. "He did walk out on my mother and me when I was three, so maybe he thinks he owes me something, that he should at least pretend he cares something about me."

"Mr. Brice is a strange man, child, and that's something you need to try to understand. Seems to me he's scared to tie himself down to one woman so he just changes girl friends as often as he changes his clothes. It's right sad, if you ask me."

"It's right disgusting," Katherine said implacably. "But I've never really expected anything better from him. He's a gambler, isn't he? And gamblers just don't have any emotions. All they want out of life is a good time, wherever and whenever they can get it."

Honey, you're so young," Mallie admonished. "You just don't know the first thing about men."

Katherine lifted her shoulders in a careless shrug again, then proceeded to remove the pins that confined her hair. Gold-streaked auburn tresses cascaded down nearly to her waist and after a quick thorough brushing, she began plaiting it into one long fat braid. Finished, she rose to her feet, that stubborn expression still on her face but she did lose most of her ill humor as Mallie regarded her with an approving smile.

"Your daddy's going to be fighting young men off with a stick this summer," the housekeeper declared. "They're going to be lining up at the front door, wanting to take you out. You're so pretty."

"Well, thank you for the compliment, but don't you believe you're a little prejudiced?" Katherine responded glibly, surveying her reflection in the full length mirror on her closet door. She supposed she looked presentable but she certainly couldn't consider herself pretty. She was a trifle too thin, despite the fairly generous swell of her breasts and the womanly curve of her hips. At least her legs were slender and shapely, she thought critically, but that wasn't enough to attract men in the vast numbers Mallie was predicting.

"Considering the abundance of really glamorous girls around Tahoe, I don't think I'll be much in demand," she said wryly and without much concern. "I doubt I'll speak to any young men the whole summer."

"Not if you hide yourself on that beach every day like you always do," Mallie agreed flatly. "You're too shy, Kit. You need to get out with other young people more."

"I have plenty of friends in Baltimore," Katherine assured her. "I miss them during the summers, but I really don't mind so much not knowing anybody here."

"It ain't right, though," Mallie persisted worriedly, handing Katherine her terry cloth beach jacket and a large beach towel. "I don't like to see you all alone all the time."

"Being alone isn't so bad," Katherine said softly. "It's better than being with people you'd really rather not be with." Scooping up the paperback book she had been reading and a small bottle of sunscreen, Katherine started for her door, smiling back over her shoulder at the housekeeper. "Don't worry about me so, Mallie. Back home, I'm not a bit antisocial. It's only here that I prefer to be alone." When Mallie shook her head resignedly and finally smiled again, Katherine tossed up one hand in a wave. "Well, I can't wait a minute longer to go for a swim so I'm going down to the beach. But I'll be back in time to get ready for dinner."

A moment later, outside on the narrow, twisting path that led through the stand of pine trees to the shore, Katherine paused, enjoying the calming silence broken only by the wind swaying the high cone-scattered branches and by the occasional clear notes of a singing bird. As she went on, her bare toes curled into the prickly carpet of pine needles, then she picked her way gingerly down the rough stone steps that led to the cove. Taking a deep breath of the sweet fresh air, she spread her towel on the coarse sand and lay down, planning to sunbathe for fifteen minutes or so before swimming.

She had lain there for several minutes, half dozing, when she suddenly became aware that the sun was no longer glaring with such bright light against her closed eyelids. They fluttered open. Her green eyes widened as they traveled in bemused fascination over long muscular legs covered with fine dark brown hair, past lean hips clad in white swimming trunks and a broad muscular chest covered by a navy polo shirt. As her eyes darted up to meet a pair of obviously amused blue ones, the man who towered over her smiled, etching deep creases into lean tanned cheeks beside his sensuously curved mouth.

With a soft startled gasp, Katherine struggled to sit up

as he suddenly dropped down on his knees beside her on the towel. Though she instinctively crossed her arms across her breasts, she managed to regain sufficient composure to glare at the gambler—Jason. As he raked lean fingers lazily through the thickness of his sun-streaked sandy hair, he didn't seem aware of her indignant expression. He was far too busy allowing his narrowed gaze to rove over her from the thick glossy auburn hair swept back from her small face down to her slim ankles and small slender feet. When his blue eyes met her green ones again, and her cheeks darkened with color, he smiled indulgently and said softly, "Hello again, Kit."

Indignation heightened the color in her cheeks. "You may call me Katherine or even Miss Delacorte," she said too primly. "But I wish you wouldn't call me Kit. It's my father's nickname for me and, to be honest, I've never particularly cared for it."

"Pity. I like the name Kit and that's what I intend to call you," Jason said flatly. "Katherine's much too formal a name for a girl with a sprinkling of freckles across her nose."

Shifting uncomfortably on the towel, Katherine had no idea how to handle this man. She didn't like the breathless tension he could create in her and she wanted him to go away and leave her alone. "What are you doing here?" she at last asked rudely. "This is a private beach."

"Oh, I don't think Brice would mind my being here," Jason replied calmly. After making himself quite comfortable by leaning back on his elbows and stretching his long strong legs out in front of him, he smiled at her again. "You know, Kit, you're not a very friendly girl."

"My mother told me never to talk to strangers," she retorted cuttingly, moving to the far edge of the beach towel. "And since I don't know you . . ."

"Jason Roarke," he introduced himself casually. "And

31

I'm not really a stranger, am I? At least you know I'm a friend of your father."

Which is the main reason I want to avoid you, she longed to retort, but she didn't. Instead, she lifted her chin defiantly. "Why aren't you somewhere sleeping?" she asked tersely. "I would think you'd be exhausted after your all-night poker game."

Jason Roarke stroked the strong line of his now clean-shaven jaw. "I was tired until I walked out on my balcony and saw you down here on the beach. Then I decided I wanted a swim before going to sleep."

"You live close by?" Katherine exclaimed softly, unaware of the dismay in her voice. "Close enough to see this cove from your balcony?"

Turning, he looked up into the trees to the right of her father's property and inclined his head. "I live in the cedar A-frame on that narrow promontory."

Katherine's gaze followed the line of his. Though the promontory was some distance away, it jutted out enough to afford him a splendid unobstructed view of the cove. Her stomach muscles tightened at the thought of him watching her from his balcony and she wondered how he could have recognized her from so far away. He must have terrific eyesight—or a pair of binoculars, she thought abruptly. Eyeing him with some suspicion, she edged herself closer to the far side of the towel. "Well, I suppose you were the big winner in your poker game," she murmured, for lack of anything better to say. "Did you teach the oil heir a lesson? Or does he still want to become a professional gambler?"

"I think he's probably shelved that idea for a while," Jason replied flatly, scooping up a large handful of sand and allowing it to sift slowly between his long lean fingers. "He was the best poker player in his frat house at college so he got the mistaken notion that he could make it as a pro. But after last night and today, he'll probably be satisfied to go back home and become a vice-president in his father's oil company."

Barely aware of what he was saying, Katherine stared at his sun-browned hands. Many gamblers she had seen over the years wore ostentatious diamond rings but Jason's fingers were mercifully bare. Actually, he wasn't like any gambler she had ever seen. There was too much warmth in his blue eyes. Of course, before he had noticed her during the game today, she had seen no emotion at all in the steely blue depths. Most gamblers couldn't turn that unfeeling look off and on at will, though. They always gazed at people with cold hard eyes and the fact that Jason was different intrigued her, despite the fact that she didn't even want to think about him. As she stared at him, a perplexed frown marring her smooth brow, she suddenly became aware that he was watching her intently, too. She blushed again and looked away hastily.

"Well, are you going to lie here in the sun all afternoon and bake wrinkles into that very nice skin or are you going swimming?" Jason asked after stifling a yawn. "I think we should go for a swim."

"I think you should go home and sleep," Katherine said nervously. "Especially if you plan to play poker again tonight."

"Oh, but I don't. I always take a few days off between big games. So let's go for that swim, hmm?"

"Be my guest," Katherine murmured without looking at him. "I think I'd like to sit here awhile longer before I go in."

"Then I'll wait too," he said, propping himself up on only one elbow as he turned over onto his side to face her. "So what shall we do? If you happen to have a deck of cards with you, we could play strip poker."

Katherine jerked her head around to stare at him, her eyes wide with astonishment. But she had no idea if his suggestion was serious or not because the steely blue

33

depths of his were suddenly unreadable again. Thoroughly confused, she muttered, "Poker is one card game I've never played."

"What do you play then?" he asked lazily. "Old Maid?"

"I play bridge occasionally," she answered with an impatient sigh, though she had detected a teasing note in his deep voice. Somehow she had to find a way to get rid of this man before he made her so nervous that he ruined the rest of her day. Already, her heart was beating erratically and the closer he came to her, the harder the pulses in her temples pounded. It wasn't only the fact that he behaved like no gambler she had ever met that disturbed her. He was also so overwhelmingly masculine that she didn't feel exactly safe in this secluded cove with him. Her anxious gaze moved over the broad expanse of his chest and she swallowed with difficulty. "Uh, why don't you just go on and have your swim. No need to wait for me," she said weakly. "I–I'd like to read for a while."

"I think we should do something together and we can't read the same book at the same time. Unless," he added, his tone suggestive, reaching out toward the Gothic romance laying on the towel, "there are some spicy love scenes in here that you think we might enjoy reading aloud to each other."

With a strangled protest, Katherine slapped his hand away and snatched up the book to thrust it beneath the towel. "Really, you're impossible," she murmured, her cheeks flaming. "Why should I want to read spicy love scenes with you, even if there were any in there?"

A strange look came into his vivid blue eyes. He reached out to brush the hair-roughened back of his hand against her hot cheek. "Don't you know when someone's teasing you, Kit?" he asked softly. "I assure you I've long since passed the age when I underlined the sexy passages in books."

She felt like a fool. Chewing her lower lip, she gazed at him, not knowing whether to apologize to him for reacting so adolescently or to simply let the incident pass.

Jason made her decision for her. Rising to his feet, with the lithe ease of a big cat, he reached down for her hand and pulled her up to stand before him. Then he led her to the gently lapping edge of the water, his fingers pressing into the small of her back to urge her forward. She trembled at the oddly intimate physical contact and waded in, simply to escape his disturbing touch. Gasping as the amazingly cold water slapped against the sensitive skin of her thighs, she didn't give herself a chance to reconsider and dived beneath the placid surface. Coming up again for breath, she glided through the silky smooth water in a brisk scissor stroke until she began to feel warm again. Jason swam at some distance from her, barely disturbing the calm surface with his strong Australian crawl and Katherine watched him out of the corner of her eye as she paddled about lazily. When it seemed he wasn't going to come in her direction, she relaxed slightly and stretched out to float on her back beneath the warming sun.

For fifteen minutes or so, she was alone. Then, suddenly, the peace was shattered. As two strong hands gripped her slender ankles, Katherine instinctively took a breath before she was unceremoniously dragged beneath the surface. Unafraid, she relaxed completely until those same strong hands spanned her bare waist. Then she struggled, resurfacing even as she pushed frantically at Jason's broad, hard chest. She could feel his heart beating steadily beneath her palms and she could see from the lazy smile curving his chiseled mouth that her efforts to escape him weren't bothering him one whit. She went limp, allowing him to keep them both afloat by treading water.

"Now that's better, isn't it?" he asked softly, his narrowed gaze lingering on the enticing swell of her breasts above the bra of her swimsuit. "You should relax more often, Kit. You're such a tense, serious little girl."

She couldn't look directly at him and when his fingers suddenly spread open over the curve of her hips, she stiffened again and foolishly renewed her struggles. Her kicking legs accidentally tangled with his and the brief contact with his upper thigh caused her breath to catch in her throat. Heat suffused her entire body and blazed crimson in her cheeks.

Gently, Jason wound her long braid around one hand, tilting her head back. His eyes darkened to as deep a blue as the sapphire water surrounding them.

"You're an enchanting little innocent, Kit," he murmured, his voice low and appealingly husky as he lowered his head.

Before she realized what he meant to do, his firm mouth covered hers gently. His hand cupped the back of her head as his arm encircled her waist, drawing her nearer to him. A strange quickening warmth uncurled inside her and her lips parted breathlessly for an instant until the rough tip of his tongue grazed against her own. With a soft gasp, she pushed away from him and swam jerkily toward the beach. Once she reached the towel, she threw herself face down on it, trembling violently, then tensing again as Jason lowered himself down beside her, his hard thigh brushing against hers in the process. Her face buried in her folded arms, she didn't know what to say or do. She simply waited for him to make the first move, but when several minutes had passed and he had said nothing at all and had hardly moved, she lifted her head cautiously.

He was stretched out on his back beside her. His eyes were closed and he seemed ridiculously relaxed until she noticed his slow, steady breathing. He was asleep! Katherine's mouth nearly fell open as she stared at his attractive face. He really was an impossible man! How could he just attack her the way he had, then drop off to sleep as if

too shy to try to initiate conversations with him. There hadn't seemed to be any common ground between them.

This morning was somewhat different, however. As Brice folded his newspaper and laid it aside, giving Katherine one of those crooked uncomfortable smiles, her curiosity could no longer be contained. She blurted out impetuously, "What do you know about Jason Roarke?"

"Jason?" Brice frowned, staring down at the tabletop thoughtfully. Then he shrugged. "I guess I really don't know a lot about him."

Katherine waited for him to tell what he did know, but when Brice said nothing more for several moments, she suppressed a frustrated sigh. Obviously, she was going to have to drag even the little information he had about Jason out of him. "Well, tell me what you do know," she finally prompted.

Still not looking at her, Brice smiled slightly to himself. "Jason's one of those mystery men we get in Tahoe occasionally. No one knows anything about him. Of course there are rumors circulating. Most people think he must have made the gambling circuit in Europe before coming here, but I've never talked to anybody who ever saw him anywhere over there. A couple of the boys flew in from Monte Carlo the other day but they'd never heard of him."

"I see," Katherine said musingly. "Well, what does it mean that nobody's ever heard of him? That he probably just started gambling professionally?"

Brice actually chuckled, a rare reaction coming from him. "I don't think he's a novice, Kit. He's much too cool. If he'd just started gambling professionally, he'd be out to make a reputation for himself. He'd make sure he was in every big game around. But Jason misses quite a few."

"Maybe he's just at one of the other casinos when he's not at Cedars."

Brice shook his head. "No, we always hear about it when he's in a game somewhere else. Jason's been the big winner here for the past two months so everything he does is news. He just isn't interested in playing in all the big games, which of course makes everybody in Tahoe even more curious about him. Half the showgirls in the revue at Cedars would give a month's salary to find out about his personal life."

Katherine leaned forward, her arms resting on the table, unable to hide her interest. "You mean he's never been out with any of the girls?"

"Oh, one or two have been out with him, not that it did them any good. He didn't tell them anything about himself. He's pretty much of a loner."

"He didn't seem like a loner to me," Katherine mused aloud, then blushed as her father shot her a sharp look. She gestured nervously. "Well, what I mean is he . . ."

"Why are you so interested in Jason Roarke anyway?" Brice questioned, his green eyes hard as they flicked over her. "Or more to the point, how do you even know who he is?"

"Oh, you know, I served the drinks to that private game he was in Tuesday," Katherine said evasively. "Remember?"

Brice nodded gravely. "I remember, but I still don't understand why you're so interested in him after only seeing him that one time."

"Well, actually, I did see him again," Katherine murmured, examining her fingernails closely. "When I was on the beach Tuesday afternoon, he joined me and we talked for a little while."

Brice's jaw tightened. "Obviously no accidental meeting since there's no continuous stretch of sand between our beach and his. I imagine he saw you there from his deck and went to all the trouble of walking through the woods to join you. Why did he do that, Kit?"

"I really don't know why," she answered honestly, baffled by her father's sharp inquisition. "Maybe he just wanted to talk to somebody."

"I doubt that. Did he ask you out, Kit? If he did, I hope you refused."

Thoroughly confused, Katherine tilted her head to one side inquiringly. "He didn't ask me out. But if he were to sometime, why would you want me to refuse? I don't understand. Don't you like him?"

"I like Jason Roarke just fine," Brice said stiffly. "I simply don't want you getting involved with him. He's at least eleven or twelve years older than you."

"That's not a vast age difference," Katherine argued, oddly irritated that her father was now telling her who she shouldn't see after all the years of not caring what she did. She thrust out her chin defiantly. "I can't see why you'd hold twelve years against him."

"It isn't the years so much, Kit," Brice said, his tone gentling somewhat. "It's more the difference in experiences. You're only twenty-one and I'm sure Jason Roarke is accustomed to women who are more mature and sophisticated than you are. I just don't think it would be a good idea for you to get involved with a man like him."

Katherine shook her head incredulously. "You know you're not making much sense, don't you? You're telling me I shouldn't get involved with a man like *you* because Jason *is* like you."

"Exactly, Kit," her father said, standing as he laid down his napkin. "That's why I know what I'm talking about. Jason Roarke isn't right for a girl like you because I wasn't right for your mother. And I'd hate for him to hurt you the way I hurt her. Now, if you'll excuse me, I have to get to the casino."

As he turned and walked out of the kitchen, Katherine stared after him, barely able to believe she had heard him correctly. He felt guilty. And she had never thought that he did.

For the next hour, Katherine considered what her father had said and began to realize he might not be as one-dimensional as she had always believed. At least, he felt some regret for the way he had treated her mother, which made Katherine wonder if perhaps he regretted his treatment of her too. He hadn't ever shown her any real affection so she had assumed he was totally unfeeling. But now she had to wonder if there could be a tiny crack in that hard veneer of his after all.

That was the question she voiced to Jess Whitney when the secretary came to the house to pick up some papers for Brice about ten o'clock the same morning. Persuading the older woman to stay for a cup of coffee before returning to the casino, Katherine positioned herself on the white sofa in the living room. "Does my father ever talk to you about me?" she asked abruptly.

After taking a cautious sip of her steaming coffee, Jess nodded, smiling. "Well, you know Brice isn't exactly a chatterbox, but he does talk about you more than anyone or anything else."

"What does he say?" Katherine murmured, almost afraid to hear. "What does he think of me?"

"He's proud of you, Kit," Jess said gently, then when she saw the doubt in Katherine's face, added, "Really, he is. He thinks you're a lovely, intelligent girl. And he loves you."

"Has he ever told you that? Or are you just assuming he does?"

"I'm not assuming anything. I *know* Brice loves you," Jess said firmly. "He doesn't have to say it in words; it's obvious you mean a great deal to him. And you should know that, Kit."

"But I don't feel that loved," Katherine explained, giving a lost little smile. "He never talks to me, never touches me. Every summer I feel like he only has me here because he thinks he should, that it's his responsibility."

"The two of you simply don't communicate at all, do you?" Jess asked sympathetically. "You're so shy and Brice . . . well, it's just so difficult for him to show his emotions. I guess he's really shy too."

"My father?" Katherine exclaimed incredulously. "Oh, I can't believe he's shy. If he was, he'd never run a casino or have so many women in his life."

Jess shook her head. "That's not necessarily true, Kit. Some people lead very superficial lives simply because they're too shy to really commit themselves to other people. It's much safer not to get involved. Of course, it's much lonelier, too. Your father is a lonely man, whether you recognize that fact or not."

Katherine couldn't argue. She had known people who only skimmed over the surface of their lives, who never sought any deeper meaning to their existence because they were scared. Yet, she had never thought of her father as being one of them, perhaps because she needed far too much from him to be objective when he never gave it. Even now, she told herself that Jess could be the one who was wrong about him. He *could* be totally unfeeling. It would be nice if they could start communicating so she could find out about him one way or the other. And perhaps it was up to her to try to get closer to him, if he would allow her to.

"Well, I have to get back to the office with these papers," Jess declared softly, intruding on Katherine's pensive thoughts. Standing, she smiled. "You know, Kit, you're such a sweet girl. I think I'll introduce you to my brother. He arrives tomorrow to spend the next two weeks with me and maybe you and he could keep each other company while he's here. His name is Brad."

"I didn't even know you had a brother."

"He's much younger than I. Twenty-seven, to be

exact." Jess grimaced comically. "Of course, he seems to think he's supposed to supervise me. He's constantly harassing me to leave Tahoe and Brice and try to make a more secure life for myself somewhere else. Though I know he means well, I do get sick of his advice. So you'd be doing me a real favor by keeping him entertained while he's here."

Standing also, Katherine shifted her feet uncomfortably, barely aware of Jess's last words. She was more concerned with her remark about being sick of unwanted advice. "Look, I . . . hope I didn't make you mad Tuesday, when *I* told you I thought you should get away from my father. I shouldn't have said anything; it wasn't my business and . . ."

"Kit, I can stand to hear well-meaning advice once or twice," Jess said wryly. "It's the ceaseless sermonizing I can't abide. So no, you didn't make me mad. Actually, it was nice to realize you care about whether I'm happy or not."

Smiling, Katherine escorted Jess to the door where the older woman hesitated, gesturing uncertainly. "Look, why don't I just even the score and give you some advice you might not want to hear. Give Brice another chance, Kit. Try to see him through less resentful eyes. Oh, I know he's never given you much reason to think he loves you, but that's only because he doesn't know how to tell you. He does love you, though, and if you could begin to see that, both of you would be so much happier. Think about it, all right?" "I've already started," Katherine admitted, returning Jess's pleased smile.

That afternoon, Katherine explored the wooded slopes above the secondary road. Wildflower manual in hand, she searched for some of the varieties she had found last June and for new ones to identify. At the edge of a thicket of trees bordering a meadow, she discovered a carpet of sky pilots, clusters of deep blue, violet-like flowers. In the meadow itself, she found her favorite from the year before, blue-eyed grass with blade-like stems and exquisite star flowers. Since they grew abundantly, she picked some and wrapped their stems in a damp paper towel to take home to put in a vase in her room. Crossing the meadow, she entered the woods again, examining a clump of pinkish white Alpine gentians, which grew at the base of an outcropping of rock, and she glanced around nervously, aware of the ever-present threat of rattlesnakes.

After recording her finds in a small notebook, she hiked on beneath the cool canopy of tall verdant pines interspersed with an occasional maple and oak tree. From where she walked, she caught glimpses between the trees of the mirror-bright blue lake shimmering in the sunlight. For a moment, even the gentle breeze stilled and she tried to imagine what these mountains had been like before gold had been discovered and men had flocked here in droves, seeking their fortunes and taking their toll of the unrivaled pristine beauty. Yet, it was still lovely here, despite man's presence and, smiling, Katherine stopped to examine the cornstalk-like leaves of some Solomon's seals. As she bent over them, touching a fingertip to a tiny, bell-shaped flower, she spied a patch of yellow peeking through the underbrush ahead of her. Her eyes widened in excitement as she realized she might have found a leopard lily, which she had somehow missed last year. Unmindful of the branches slapping her bare legs, she plowed through the brush, delighted to discover not one but three spotted lilies. But as she reached out to touch the delicate petals, she suddenly saw something slither on the ground beside her. She panicked. Biting back a scream, she straightened too fast and proceeded to trap herself there by entangling her long braid of hair in the tenacle-like branches of a bush. Unable to get away, she looked around frantically, terrified she would find an entire family of reptilian monsters poised to strike at her feet. Even when she saw no sign of the snake, she was in a panic to escape. She yanked her braid from the viney branches, wincing as a few strands clung tenaciously and had to be extricated by trembling fingers.

After freeing herself completely, Katherine stumbled through the underbrush out onto the trail again, then wasted no time putting as much distance as possible between herself and the slithery, revolting creature. To add insult to injury, she tripped over an exposed tree root in her hasty undignified retreat. Muttering crossly, she landed on all fours, grinding the dark loamy soil into her knees and hands. She rose to her feet, surveying her scraped left knee, taking care not to brush her filthy hands against her crisp khaki shorts. More frustrated now than scared, she pushed an untidy strand of hair back from her temple with the back of her hand as she marched directly to one of the icy-cold mountain streams that fed the lake. Without soap, her ablutions were only partially successful and she flinched as the water stung her tender knee. Though she managed to cleanse her hands thoroughly, along with her uninjured knee, her scraped flesh still bore lingering traces of grime and would until she had a proper bath with soap and warm water.

Hot and bothered, she trudged down the trail, reaching the road about a half mile from her father's house. Leaning against the massive trunk of an ancient western juniper, she flexed her knee gingerly. Then knowing she wasn't going to get home by lounging around, she began walking.

She had hobbled along the curving road for about two hundred yards when a car slowed down behind her. Glancing back over her shoulder curiously, she squinted at the sunlight reflecting glaringly on the hood of a silver Jaguar. It wasn't until the car drew up along side her that she recognized the driver.

"Well, Kit, you look as if you need[...]" Jason Roarke declared, giving her a slow, [...] "Care for a ride home?"

As he stopped the Jaguar on the shoulder beside her, Katherine gazed rather longingly at the black leather passenger seat. After her misadventure in the woods, she was hot and tired and in no mood to walk another step today. Yet she wondered how wise it would be to get into a car alone with *him*. He could be a dangerous man as she had discovered Tuesday afternoon. Still, it wasn't a long drive to her father's house and since she really didn't want to walk . . .

After opening the door and dropping into the leather bucket seat with a sigh of relief, Katherine rubbed her burning knee and glanced warily at Jason. Her cheeks grew pink as she met his appraising blue eyes. Why did he have to look so infuriatingly neat in white tennis shorts and white knit shirt when she looked like something the cat had dragged in? As his narrowed gaze traveled the length of her tensed body mercilessly and a smile tugged at the corners of his sensuously carved lips, she turned away hastily, unable to withstand such intense scrutiny.

"I didn't even know there were grizzlies up in those woods," Jason commented as he turned the Jaguar out onto the road again. "And I certainly didn't know you made a habit of wrestling them."

"Very funny," Katherine muttered defensively, automatically trying to smooth the strands of hair that had been pulled from her loose messy braid. Thrusting out her small chin, she glared at Jason indignantly. "I just hope your driving doesn't make me wish I was somewhere wrestling a grizzly. Since it doesn't bother you to take chances with your money, I wonder if you feel the same way about your life. Hopefully, you don't drive like a maniac."

Jason's laughter came from deep in his throat and he

ulgence. "I assure you I'm a
the death defying stunts to race
money is one thing. I've never
my life. I enjoy living too much."

Katherine murmured disapproving-
life was one long party. When her
no response, however, she looked up at
rised to see that his expression had sobered.

"I get the impression that you don't care for gamblers," he said at last, glancing at her, his blue eyes intent. "Or is it just me you don't care for?"

"It's gamblers in general," Katherine answered honestly. "And it isn't that I don't care for them. It's just that I have no idea what makes them tick."

"Not even your father?" Jason questioned gently. "Don't you understand him?"

"I understand him least of all," Katherine responded stiffly, unaware of the detectable hint of bitterness in her tone. "Of course, he's not the easiest person in the world to get to know. I suppose no gambler is."

"Don't make hasty generalizations," Jason cautioned. "All gamblers aren't alike, Kit. For example, I'd be happy to let you get to know me better, if only you'd give yourself a chance."

There was a suggestive note in his deep voice that set her pulses pounding. Chewing her lower lip, she clenched her hands together in her lap to still their ridiculous shakiness and stared out her window. Then as the Jaguar zipped right past her father's house, her eyes widened and she spun around in her seat to face Jason again. "You missed the drive!"

"So I did," he drawled laconically, glancing at her, laughter dancing in his eyes. "Don't look at me like I've abducted you for some nefarious purpose, Kit. I'm only taking you to my house."

48

"But I don't want to go to your house!" she exclaimed softly, an odd mixture of fear and excitement causing her heart to thud jerkily. "I need to go home and bandage my knee. See, I scraped it."

He nodded, glancing over at her again. But it was on the smooth length of her slender thigh, not her injured knee, that his gaze lingered. "I noticed you'd hurt yourself," he murmured at last. "But we can attend to your knee at my house." He lifted a silencing hand as she opened her mouth to protest. "No need to thank me. I'll be happy to play medic. Besides, I have your towel and book and I'm sure you want them back."

He was incorrigible, Katherine thought with a toss of her head as she looked away from him.

"Well, don't you want them back?" he persisted. "Or had you forgotten I took them after you deserted me on the beach Tuesday afternoon? Why did you leave like that anyway? You should have awakened me."

Ignoring his last words, she glared at him, appalled by the effortless way he could arouse all sorts of violent emotions in her. "I haven't forgotten you took my book, Mr. Roarke. I'd only read half of it so, of course, I want it back. I'd like to see how it ends."

"I read it," he announced abruptly, his blue eyes impaling the soft green of hers for an instant. "In fact, I took it deliberately for that purpose. I thought I'd discover what Kit Delacorte is really like. You can tell a great deal about a person by the kind of books he or she reads."

"Can you really?" she responded tersely, trying to conceal the sudden vulnerability she felt. "I wasn't aware that reading habits were so revealing."

"They are. For example, I now know you're an incurable romantic," Jason said dryly, swinging the silver Jaguar off the road onto a winding asphalt drive. "You're much like the heroine in your Gothic romance—shy but feisty and seeking love. And I'm sure you seek a man like your heroine found—the dark, brooding, misunderstood hero who saves her from the clutches of his murderous cousin just in the nick of time. Then he admits he has loved her from afar during all their trying times and now wants to marry and protect her for the rest of their lives. That's the kind of man you want, isn't it, Kit? Someone strong to take care of you?"

Unable to look at him, Katherine swallowed convulsively, amazed and disconcerted by his perceptiveness. It was almost as if he could read her mind and since he was so like the man in her fantasies, at least in appearance, his insight was doubly disturbing. "Just because I read a few Gothic romances, you shouldn't assume I identify with the heroines," she said weakly. "I—I don't."

"Don't you?" he persisted gently, stopping the car beneath the stand of towering pines before his large cedar A-frame house. Turning in his seat, he observed her, then amazingly reached out to brush the back of his hand against her porcelain cheek. "Come on, Kit, you can't tell me you're not looking for a strong supportive hero-type to fall in love with."

"Well, what if I am?" she retorted defensively, too disturbed by his caress. "What's wrong with that?"

"Nothing," he answered softly, seriously. "But it's not very pleasant for me to know you don't include me in the hero-type category."

Detecting nearly genuine regret in his tone, Katherine surveyed his lean, sun-browned face. "It . . . it's nothing personal," she stammered. "You're just a gambler and I . . ."

"And you don't trust gamblers," he finished for her. "Do you, Kit?" When she shook her head, he suddenly smiled mischievously. "I have to remind you our heroine didn't trust our hero, either. Remember? It was only near the end that she realized how wrong she'd been about him. So don't you think you could possibly be wrong about me?"

Katherine had no answer to such a logical question as Jason got out of the car, then came around to open her door. She gazed up at him bewilderedly and though she didn't resist as he took her hand and helped her out, she muttered uneasily, "I should go home. Really, I . . ."

"What's wrong?" he interrupted, squeezing her hand lightly before releasing it. "I think you're afraid of me, Kit."

"I am not," she protested, squaring her shoulders. "I . . . have no reason to be afraid of you, do I?"

"None whatsoever," he answered, cupping her elbow in one large hand, guiding her toward his front door.

Committed now by her foolish show of bravado, Katherine went with him willingly. But as she glanced at Jason's chiseled profile, her common sense informed her that she'd be far wiser to take off running through the woods toward home, as if the devil himself were chasing at her heels.

Chapter Four

The interior of Jason's house possessed a rustic charm. Richly paneled walls and the high cathedral ceiling, crisscrossed by exposed cedarwood beams created a comfortable warmth in the great room. A Navajo rug, woven in the earthy hues of russet and brown covered the pegged wooden floor before the huge stone fireplace. The sofa was upholstered in a patchwork of blue, brown and russet and two sky blue easy chairs looked cool and comfortably inviting. There was a massive antique roll-top desk dominating one of the inside walls, on which were displayed several High Sierra landscapes painted by local artists.

As Jason started to guide Katherine across the hardwood floor toward the sofa, she dragged her feet, not that it did her any good. His hand cupping her elbow simply tightened beneath her arm, impelling her forward.

"Sit down," he commanded gently, his hard fingers grazing the sensitive inner flesh of her forearm as he relinquished his hold on her. "I'll go get the first aid kit and attend to that knee."

Katherine's wide green eyes followed him as he strode through a swinging door at the far end of the room. Taking a deep shuddering breath, she started unweaving her mussed braid, planning to redo it neatly before he returned. But he came back too soon, carrying a metal basin half filled with warm soapy water and a white red-crossed box tucked under his arm. As he knelt down on the Navajo rug before Katherine, she tensed and her breathing quickened as she gazed down at his golden, sunstreaked hair as he bent his head. With sterile cotton soaked in the warm sudsy water, he removed the remaining traces of dirt ground into her roughened skin. When the sting of the soap made her flinch once, he glanced up at her, wincing commiserately.

"I'm trying not to hurt you," he said softly, in way of apology as he continued bathing her knee. "But that humus soil up in those woods is probably loaded with all kinds of unpleasant bacteria. So it's important to cleanse this scrape as thoroughly as possible."

"I know," she murmured, watching as he used a sterile gauze pad to blot dry her skin. Then her breath caught in her throat and she closed her eyes as his fingertips grazed over the sensitized reddened knee. She had never imagined a man's touch could be so gentle while at the same time evoking a shivery thrill of delight that coursed throughout her body. Her thickly-fringed eyes flickered open and she had to squeeze her hands tightly together in her lap to prevent herself from reaching out to touch his thick hair as he smoothed an antibacterial salve onto her knee, then lightly taped a gauze bandage over it. He was finished and she expected him to move away from her but he remained where he was, his narrowing gaze holding hers. She drew in a startled breath as he suddenly curved his hand around the trim ankle of her uninjured leg and when his rough fingertips began to blaze a fiery trail up over the shapely contour of her calf, she trembled violently. She should push his hand away; she knew she should, yet somehow she couldn't force herself to do it. His touch was creating rivers of molten fire in her veins and the unfamiliar sensation was so pleasurable that she felt a dizzying, frightening desire to go on experiencing it forever. Nearly hypnotized by the smoldering light in his dark blue eyes, she was possessed by the insane desire to reach out and tangle her fingers exploringly in the thickness of his hair.

"Kit," he murmured huskily, then cursed beneath his breath as a scurrying commotion behind the swinging door shattered the evocative moment. He rose to his feet as a leggy yellow dog catapulted herself across the room toward him, her entire body trembling as she softly yipped with the joy of seeing him.

"Sit, Georgia," he commanded firmly. To Katherine's amazement, the ecstatic yellow and cream Labrador sat to gaze up at him with soulful, adoring black eyes, her strong tail beating a tattoo on the hardwood floor.

"Oh, Jason, she's beautiful," Katherine said softly, holding out her fingers for the dog's approving sniff. "Is she yours?"

Nodding, he gave a comical grimace. "I just happened to be at the wrong place at the wrong time. When I was walking past a pet shop, I suddenly found myself being gazed at balefully by those soft black eyes. She just looked so sad, sitting there behind that window that I . . . Well, it's obvious she began manipulating me that very minute."

Deliberately avoiding looking up at him, Katherine scratched behind the grateful dog's ears, surprised once again by a new facet of Jason's personality. Gamblers, in general, including her father, weren't a sentimental lot and Katherine was intrigued by the fact that Jason was tenderhearted enough to be manipulated by a small furry animal, however pretty that animal might be. Yet, intrinsically honest as she was, especially with herself, she had to admit that Jason Roarke had intrigued her from the very first moment they had met. He was a fascinating enigma, too fascinating, she thought pensively, for her peace of mind. She had no idea what to expect of him at any given time and her uncertainty about him made her exceedingly nervous. Even now, she sensed he was watching her intently, but she was afraid to look up, unwilling to try to interpret the usually unreadable message in his eyes. Instead, she chose to push her disturbing thoughts to the back of her mind and, attempting to keep conversation light and impersonal, she asked, "Why did you name her Georgia?"

"When I bought her, her coat reminded me of a Georgia peach."

"It still looks like that," Katherine noted, stroking the dog's short fuzzy fur. "It's so soft, like a puppy's."

"She is still a puppy," Jason informed her, smiling at her surprised expression. "She's only five months old, give or take a few days."

"Really?" Katherine examined the leggy dog whose shoulders already reached her knees. "Good heavens, how big will she be when she's full grown then?"

"Heaven only knows," Jason answered, shrugging resignedly. "I'm just hoping I won't need to build a stable to keep her in."

Katherine laughed, her green eyes sparkling up at him impishly. "Well, if she does grow to be horse-sized, she'll undoubtedly be listed in the Guinness Book of World Records and you'll be listed, too, as her proud owner. Won't that make you deliriously happy?"

"Not if I have to starve to keep her fed," he retorted wryly, tugging a strand of Katherine's hair that still cascaded like a russet curtain down around her bare arms.

His fingers lingered in the silken tress, exploring the soft texture with his fingertips. Then as he sought her bemused gaze with his darkening blue eyes, a sudden ardent glow flared in the gold-flecked depths.

Recognizing the danger signal immediately, Katherine started to draw away but at that moment, Georgia inadvertently rescued her. Wriggling between the two pairs of legs, she gazed up hopefully at Jason, her limpid black eyes begging for attention.

He sighed rather impatiently and reached for Katherine's hand, drawing her up to stand before him. "Let's walk down to the lake," he suggested, shaking his head at the overgrown puppy gamboling at his feet. "Maybe she'll chase a butterfly or something there."

Katherine knew she shouldn't have gone with him. Yet the firm pressure of his hard fingers entwined with hers induced in her a curious lethargy that forestalled all the sensible objections she knew she should make. Her legs felt oddly weak as she walked with him out the open sliding glass doors onto the lower deck where the floor of the balcony above provided a ceiling. The fragrance of the pines combined with the fresh lime scent of his aftershave and as they followed a pebbled path down to the shore, she felt almost as if she were lost in one of her fantasies. Though she knew Jason was nothing like the men she daydreamed about, he seemed to be. He seemed strong, commanding, yet capable of tenderness. But she knew that must be only the impression he gave. Beneath that attractive facade, he had to be shallow. He had to be, she told herself sternly. He was a gambler, wasn't he?

On the coarse beach, Jason and Katherine found a shady spot beneath a young hemlock tree. They sat down and as he stretched his long powerful legs out in front of him, she wrapped her arms around her drawn-up legs and rested her chin on her uninjured knee, realizing even as she did it, that she was assuming an obviously self-protecting posture. For several long minutes they said nothing to each other and sat silently watching Georgia avidly dig potholes in the sand. As the puppy accidentally sniffed some particles of dirt into her nostrils, then sneezed violently, Jason chuckled softly and shook his head.

Katherine smiled at him, feeling some of the tension was now eased. "What's she looking for?"

"Nothing in particular, probably," he answered, his gaze wandering over Katherine with disconcerting intensity. "I suppose she's just searching, hoping she'll find something of value. And it's really not that different from the searching we humans do, is it, Kit?"

"Oh, that's too philosophical a question for me," she responded, attempting to be flippant, but not altogether successful. She lifted her hand uneasily. "I mean, I think I'll leave questions like that to the behavioral scientists."

"Why? Don't you ever want to delve into human nature, if for no other reason than to find out more about who you are?"

She eyed him with blatant curiosity, consumed by the desire to understand him. Philosophy and psychology were two of the least likely subjects she had ever expected a gambler to discuss. Didn't they all live for the pleasures of the moment and say to hell with the deeper intrinsic meanings of existence? Until meeting Jason, she had assumed that was every gambler's code of living but now she was beginning to wonder if he could be the exception to the rule. Or, she reminded herself firmly, he could simply be trying to con her into believing he was less shallow than she assumed he must be. If he was conning her, however, he was a consummate actor. He seemed totally sincere, yet her acquired distrust of gamblers made her reluctant to allow herself to believe him.

Perhaps her expression conveyed that reluctance because Jason abruptly heaved a sigh and shook his head.

"Why don't you tell me why you have this intense aversion to gamblers, Kit?" he questioned bluntly. "I assume it has something to do with your relationship with your father. Right?"

"Right," she replied, too surprised again by his perceptiveness to even try to deny the truth. Resting her chin on her knee once again, she stared out unseeingly at the lake. "He left us. When I was three, he just walked out on Mother and me so he could be free to gamble and chase after women. So, I have no reason to have a high regard for men like him."

"All men aren't alike, Kit," Jason reminded her gently. "And even though you don't want to believe me, all gamblers aren't alike, either. "Just because your father was irresponsible in his younger years, you can't automatically assume that I am, too."

"Then how can you live the way you do?" she exclaimed softly, searching his lean brown face rather desperately. "How can you move from one high stakes game to another, risking more money in one night than many people earn in a whole year? What's the point in it? What kind of contribution are you making?"

"What kind of contribution would you like to make, Kit?" he countered, slickly evading her question. "What is it you want to do with your life?"

Put on the defensive again, she shrugged. "I don't know exactly, yet. Help people make their lives better somehow, I guess. I'm not sure precisely how. I've considered becoming a physical therapist or a teacher of handicapped children."

"Admirable ambitions," he said without a trace of mockery. "I'm sure you'd excel in either occupation. And I think either occupation would be good for you, too. You need to free that warm, loving nature you try so hard to hide beneath a cool, reserved exterior."

She had no answer for that and uncomfortable with the

entire discussion, she hastily changed the subject. "You know the other day on the beach, when you introduced yourself, I thought I'd heard your name before," she babbled. "Later, I remembered that I had. Did you realize there's also a novelist named Jason Roarke? He couldn't possibly be your father, could he?"

"No, he isn't my father," Jason said, his steady gaze holding hers. "But I have heard of him, though I must admit I've never bought one of his books. Have you?"

"Oh, yes, and you should, too," Katherine declared enthusiastically. "He's an excellent storyteller and his characters are so real. His writing style is simple and very direct. You don't get confused and have to flip back through the pages you've already read to see if there was something you missed. And though he writes about all kinds of people, he makes you realize they're all basically the same, that they all want love and a sense of self-worth. Oh, he's really an enjoyable writer. I could let you borrow one of his novels if you'd like to read it."

"Maybe I will," Jason said, a hint of a smile tugging at his firm lips. "And maybe you should consider a career as a critic. It would be refreshing to read a complimentary review occasionally. All critics seem to find a perverse joy in picking every writer's work to pieces. I'm sure Mr. Roarke would appreciate you."

"Some critics do seem to delight in being nasty, don't they?" Katherine agreed with a grin. "But I guess no one would read them if they heaped praise on every book they reviewed."

"And bad reviews often increase sales," Jason added. "At least, that's what I've heard."

Feeling infinitely more relaxed now, Katherine stretched her own legs out in front of her and rested back on her elbows. Just as she started to ask Jason what kind of books he did read, Georgia, tired of her fruitless excavations, and catching a small stick in her mouth, loped across the sand toward them. She skidded to a halt before Jason, her entire back section wagging as her mournful black eyes implored him to play with her.

"Conned again," Jason drawled, rising to his feet with a sheepish smile. Then he strode along the beach near the water's edge and at his command, Georgia relinquished the stick to him.

To Katherine's surprise, Jason pitched the stick far out into the lake. Then Georgia bounded in after it without hesitation and paddled away from the shore, only her sleek yellow head visible above the blue surface. She returned the stick to Jason automatically, then waited impatiently for him to throw it again. The exercise was repeated several times but soon Katherine lost interest in the dog's performance. She was too enthralled by the way the muscles in Jason's shoulders rippled with each powerful toss of the stick. Almost against her will, Katherine allowed her gaze to wander down the long length of his muscular legs. Then when his exertions beneath the hot sun caused him to shed his knit shirt, she stared at his broad bronzed back and her eyes widened as a sudden intense desire to touch his smooth skin rose in her. She looked away hastily, appalled by the unusual erotic meandering of her imagination. Scooping up a handful of sand, she let it trickle slowly between her fingers and chided herself for not holding a tighter rein on her emotions.

Lost in thought, she was only half aware that Jason was walking back toward her. After Georgia shook her entire body to rid her coat of excess water, she loped along beside him. Then, still full of energy, she suddenly bounded forward, too much a puppy yet to control her exuberance. With the speed of a gazelle, she bore down on Katherine and threw herself against her, slamming her backward in a misguided effort to be friendly. It was an invitation to play but unexpected and Katherine hit the ground with such force that her breath was knocked from her. Nothing hurt; she simply couldn't catch her breath for a moment. Stunned, she closed her eyes as Georgia whimpered plaintively and nuzzled her cheek, instinctively aware of her mistake. But she scurried away, her ears down, her proud tail tucked between her legs, the moment Jason issued a strident command.

Katherine's eyes fluttered open and she attempted a wan smile as Jason dropped to his knees beside her.

"Kit, are you okay?" he muttered roughly. "You just missed hitting your head on a rock by less than an inch."

She nodded, reaching back over her head to touch the rough surface of the stone close behind her. "A miss is as good as a mile, I guess," she whispered, still rather breathless. "And I'm okay, really." Then without stopping to consider the possible consequences of her action, she lifted her hand and stroked a trembling fingertip along the fascinating crease in his cheek beside his mouth. Blue fire blazed in his eyes, immediately alerting her to the danger. Her hand dropped away.

"Kit!" he whispered hoarsely.

"No!" she gasped, but it was too late. His mouth descended swiftly, covering hers with arousing demand. His fingers tangled in the silky skein of her auburn hair as he cradled the back of her head in the cup of his hand. Firm caressing lips tugged hers apart, exerting a twisting pressure that opened her mouth to the onslaught of his. Agonizingly keen desire flickered to life deep inside her, then blazed forth. Raging flames consumed her body, igniting every nerve ending, scorching every inch of her skin, making his every touch both pleasure and pain. His tongue probed the softness of the lips clinging to his, then invaded the warm, sweet moistness within her mouth. He groaned, his long, lean body crushing her down into the warm sand.

He controlled her completely. A delicious warmth spread throughout Katherine's lower limbs. As his hot possessive kisses conquered her, deepening demandingly, she became fluid warmth beneath him, responding hesitantly at first, then with a wild abandon that would have shocked her had she been able to think. But she was beyond rational thought. All she could do was feel. Her slender arms wrapped around his strong neck and she strained her young body against him, delighting in the hair-roughened tautness of his thigh imprisoning the smooth slender length of her own.

She gloried in his masterful awakening of her senses. It was as if she had waited forever for this moment and her small fingers entwined in the thick golden hair on his nape, urging a rougher taking of her mouth.

"Kit, give me a chance to be gentle," he whispered roughly. But as he dragged his mouth from hers, her lips clung eagerly to the firm curve of his and her eyes flickered open, softly aglow with beckoning innocence. His desire to be gentle was consumed in the raging fire her acquiescence kindled. His hard lips captured hers again with bruising force. Unsteady fingers lowered the narrow straps of her camisole top, tugging the cotton knit fabric down until the top barely covered the peaks of the firm mounds of flesh his mouth sought. The rough tip of his tongue tantalized the scented shadowed hollow until she was lost in a world of sensual pleasure, feeling truly a woman for the first time in her life. She made a sound that was almost a whimper and Jason lifted his head. "Kit, are you sure you know what you're doing?" he groaned. Yet before she could answer, he wound her hair around his hand, holding her fast as his marauding mouth plundered the soft sweetness of hers again. His hand slipped beneath the hem of her camisole, seeking the entrancing insweep of her waist. As she moved feverishly beneath him, his long sensitive fingers grazed upward, taking possesion of the firm fullness of her breasts. He stroked the rounded curves, his fingers conveying barely restrained desire. The hot tumescent peaks surged against his palm and he whispered her name, his rough tone a warning.

"*Katherine,* I *need* you! So badly," he muttered hoarsely. His unsteady fingers sought the button on the waistband of her shorts as his warm breath feathered over her lips. "If you're afraid, stop me now or you may not be able to stop me at all."

His words and his fingertips grazing her sensitized abdomen brought her back to reality with a sickening jolt. A fear as old as the ages awakened in her as she remembered he was a man who could take whatever she offered, then never give her another thought as long as he lived. For some reason, he was offering an escape and she had to take it. With a cry muffled against his shoulder, she stilled his hand, shame and self-loathing rushing over her with the full realization of what she had done. She pushed at him and struggled free, turning over onto her side, unable to prevent a muffled groan from escaping her lips. Ashamed she had behaved so wantonly, she thought she'd never be able to forgive herself. She could hear Jason's ragged breathing begin to slow as he lay on his back beside her, then she tensed as his hand closed on her shoulder, turning her to him.

"For heaven's sake, don't cry," he murmured, stroking her flushed cheek with the back of his hand, frowning as she flinched. "Kit, I wasn't going to do anything you didn't want."

Blushing, she shook her head. "I know that," she whispered miserably, tears welling up in her eyes. "But I was almost willing. Until the last minute, I wanted . . . " Pressing her lips firmly together, she muttered, "I can't ever let that happen again. I can't let myself be used."

Jason's jaw tightened. The warmth in his eyes vanished and he surveyed her coldly. "Used, Kit? You really think that's all I wanted to do? Gratify purely physical desires? You don't have a very high opinion of me, do you?"

Unable to face the accusing light in his eyes, she flung her arm across her own. "I just know what kind of life you lead," she mumbled. "I know what kind of women you're accustomed to. If . . . if I had let you . . . if you had made love to me, it wouldn't have meant any more to you than it does when you make love to one of them. But I . . . Oh, Jason, our values are just so different and I hate myself for not remembering that before . . . before things went so far."

"What a child you are, Kit," he said harshly, getting to his feet, then hauling her up beside him. His scorching blue eyes bore into the soft depths of hers. "I knew you had a childlike quality about you, but I made the mistake of assuming you were a woman in some ways, too. But you aren't. You're just a timid little girl and far too young for me. Come on, I'll take you home where you can hide safely in your room."

Devastated by his caustic evaluation of her, Katherine longed to say something, anything, to him as he marched her up the path to his car. But her words could find no voice even as he drove her home, braking with such violence before her father's house, that a cloud of dust rose up from the back wheels. She glanced at the hard, implacable line of his jaw and a suddenly defensive anger overcame the guilt and shame she felt. As he reached across her to open her door and his arm grazed the rounded swell of her breasts, she shrank away from him. The mocking smile he gave her was the final straw. "I knew all along I couldn't trust you," she whispered furiously. "And don't you dare tell me I'm a little girl when you're just a little boy who won't do anything except spend your life playing silly games with a bunch of other men who don't want to accept responsibility."

His lips thinned to a grim line. "Watch what you say to me, Kit," he threatened, his voice ominously low. "Or I may be tempted to show you I am a man, in a way you won't soon forget."

Though her heartbeat quickened, she tossed her head defiantly. "I'd love to see you try," she challenged, but had enough sense to make a hasty exit from the car. She slammed the door behind her and marched up the steps of her father's house, grumbling beneath her breath as she heard Jason turn the Jaguar around and leave.

"I knew he was a cad," she muttered as she slammed into the house. "Impossible man." Still caught up in defensive indignation, she marched to the phone and called Jess Whitney, inviting her and her brother out to dinner with her father and herself the next evening. The invitation was readily accepted and when Katherine replaced the receiver, she was smiling grimly. Jason Roarke might think he was the only man in the world but she'd show him.

Chapter Five

Katherine had never been so bored in her life. Since her father and Jess hadn't been able to get away for dinner, it was now Katherine's responsibility to entertain the brother—no easy task. Much to her dismay, Brad Whitney was a dullard; there was no more polite way to put it. Tall and thin, he was a fairly attractive man, at least in appearance, but his personality left much to be desired. Though she had chosen one of the most elegant, dignified restaurants in Tahoe, Brad had nothing but complaints about it.

"It's too dark in here," he grumbled, exaggeratingly peering at his menu. "How are we supposed to read this thing without light?"

Katherine forced a wan smile, wondering why he couldn't see when she could read the menu he held perfectly well. "I think they just use a few lamps and the candles on the tables to provide a romantic atmosphere. And I think it's romantic in here, don't you?"

"Romantic?" He glanced up at her, frowning as if he didn't know what the word meant. Inconvenient, if you ask me, having to strain your eyes to see."

Katherine heaved a silent sigh, toying with the cord tie of her kelly green jersey dress, the one she had chosen to wear tonight because she thought it was the most sophisticated garment she owned. The low scalloped neckline exposed just a hint of the rounded curve of her breasts, but even that demure evidence of her femininity had seemed to embarrass Brad when they had met in the restaurant foyer for dinner. So much for trying to look sophisticated and beautiful, she thought wryly. She might as well have worn a gunny sack.

"I suppose we'll have to sit through some flashy floor show after we finish dinner," Brad intruded on her thoughts with a snort. "One of those where half-naked girls parade back and forth on stage."

"If you'd like to stay and see the girls, I guess we can," Katherine answered perversely. "I hadn't planned on that, but if you're really looking forward to it . . ."

"Well, no, I didn't say that," Brad blustered. Then his thin lips pressed together in a disapproving line. "I can assure you I have no desire to watch such a disgusting exhibition. The kind of girls that would dance in a show like that certainly don't appeal to me."

"And what kind of girls do you mean?" Katherine questioned, striving to hold onto her patience. "If you meant that as an insult, then I want to tell you that some of the girls who dance in the lounges at Cedars are very nice people."

"Hmmph, nice and cheap, probably," Brad pronounced, glancing up at the maître d' who stepped up to the table at that moment. Without consulting Katherine, he imperiously ordered every course, ending with the entree of filet of sole.

"I hope you like sole," he finally remembered to ascertain after the maître d' had already gone. "I do."

Bully for you, she longed to snap at him, but since the evening was only beginning, she held her tongue. Yet it was impossible to interject a note of friendliness in her tone when she answered him. "I like sole, but I despise barley soup. I would have preferred cream of pea."

"Barley's better for you," he announced, scraping his fingers through his short, dishwater-brown hair. "And I suggest we pass up the rich desserts and have fruit to end our meal. Processed sugar is bad for the teeth, you know."

"Oh, that's right, you're a dentist, aren't you?" Katherine said hastily, hoping he would begin a non-stop monologue about his profession so she wouldn't have to listen or make replies.

Her hopes were realized. All during dinner, Brad regaled her with his experiences from his first day of dental school to the last day he had spent in his private office before coming to Tahoe to visit Jess. Katherine had only to nod occasionally while she ate, though it was a miracle she didn't doze off to sleep as he relentlessly detailed his rather mundane life's story from birth up to the present time. All in all, it was one of the most boring meals Katherine had ever endured, yet she had no idea how to end the evening early without seeming rude.

After coffee, Brad suggested they dance. After he had led her to the gleaming dance floor off to one side from the dining room, Katherine reluctantly allowed him to take her in his arms. Almost immediately, he began to cast furtive glances at the hint of cleavage exposed at the scalloped neckline of her dress. His thin arm round her waist tightened, drawing her closer and reluctant to move nearer to him, she nearly stumbled over his feet. Unfortunately, that enabled him to glide his hand upward until his palm curved against the side of her breast.

Katherine had never been able to abide sneaks. Tensing, she stepped back from him, her green eyes flashing as they met the weak brown of his. "Don't do that again, Brad," she commanded tersely, gaining some grim satisfaction at seeing his cheeks darken with color.

"Sorry," he muttered, dropping his hand loosely to her waist again. He shrugged. "But you are a pretty girl, Kathy, so you can't really blame me."

"We just met tonight," she reminded him, beginning to dislike him intensely. "And this is just a dinner date, nothing more."

"It could be more eventually," he suggested, his gaze darting surreptitiously to her cleavage again. "Jess sure would like you and me to spend a lot of time together while I'm here. And now that I've seen you, I think that's a fine idea. So why don't we go fishing together tomorrow? I know a nice little private cove. How about it?"

Thinking she would rather go fishing with a barracuda, Katherine shook her head, though she did make an attempt to smile apologetically. "Sorry, but I have plans for tomorrow."

"Tomorrow night then?"

"I have plans then, too."

To avoid the possibility that he would ask her out the day after, she blurted out the first thing that popped into her mind. "I guess Jess is enjoying having you here. Since you live so far apart, I don't suppose you get to see all that much of each other."

"We could," Brad said, snorting derisively again. "I've tried often enough to get her to leave this place and come live with me in Philadelphia, but she doesn't have enough sense to do it. I keep telling her she's a fool to stay here, but she can't seem to drag herself away from . . . " His words halted abruptly as he noticed Katherine was paying no attention to what he said. "Hey, are you listening to me or am I just talking to myself?"

Katherine was barely aware of his impatient query. Her

eyes were riveted on a couple dancing across the room. A strange tightness developed in her chest as she watched Jason draw a beautiful statuesque blonde close against his lean body, then lower his head to whisper something into her ear. As the blonde responded with a provocative smile, Katherine experienced her first dagger-sharp stab of jealousy. What had Jason said to that woman to make her smile that way, she asked herself, agonizing over the possible answers that relentlessly bombarded her brain. Then she shook her head and, hating herself for succumbing to such a petty emotion, she forced herself to turn her attention back to Brad.

"I'm sorry," she apologized absently. "I'm afraid I didn't hear what you were saying."

"That's plenty obvious," he retorted, his thin face tight with irritation. "I was saying Jess can't seem to drag herself away from Brice, although she has to know it's stupid to stay with him. I've certainly told her that a million times. And you even told her she should leave, didn't you?"

"Yes, but I realize now I shouldn't have," Katherine answered candidly. "I had no right to try to tell her what to do. Her personal life is none of my business."

"Well, it's mine, let me tell you," Brad said huffily. "She may be older than I am, but she's still my sister. And I don't intend to sit around without saying a word while she lets Brice Delacorte use her. She must be out of her mind to think she loves him anyway. He's a worthless playboy and I wouldn't be surprised to learn he's a drunkard and a drug addict, too."

"Now, wait just a minute," Katherine protested softly, her temper erupting as she glared up at Brad's pinched face. "Do I have to remind you that you're talking about my father? Oh, he has his faults; I'm the first to admit that, but I can tell you that he is not a drug user or a drunkard, as you so crudely put it. And I don't appreciate you assuming he is, just because you don't like him. If Jess loves him, there must be something good about him."

"I doubt that," Brad countered, undaunted by her anger. "A lot of women fall for no-good bums for some strange reason. Maybe Jess is just too blind to see that, to him, women are nothing more than warm bodies."

"You sanctimonious prig!" Katherine gasped softly, her green eyes flashing dangerously. "You dare say that about him after *you* tried to paw me only two hours after we met. At least my father's honest about what he wants from women, which is more than I can say for you. You're a hypocrite. You try to sound so moralistic, then sneakily manhandle a girl when she doesn't expect it. Well, I'm not a bit surprised Jess gets so tired of hearing sermons from you."

Before Brad could stop spluttering and answer, Katherine pushed his arm from her waist and flounced away, too riled to even look where she was going. Suddenly she collided forcefully with a hard, unyielding object and strong hands clamped her upper arms. Her wide startled eyes darted upward and she had to bite back a groan as she looked up into Jason's unsmiling face. All she needed now to make the evening a perfectly horrendous disaster was to become embroiled in another confrontation with him.

"Shall we dance, Kit?" he murmured astoundingly. Taking acquiescence for granted, he slipped his left arm around her narrow waist and took her small right hand firmly in his, smoothly leading her into step with the slow, hypnotic beat of the music.

Despite Katherine's desire to be cool and aloof, she simply couldn't manage it. Dancing with Jason was far different from dancing with Brad. Jason's arm encircling her waist exerted a confident yet gentle pressure. Her fingertips, curved over his shoulders, encountered his corded muscles through the linen fabric of his sand-colored vested suit. Somehow, she felt safe in his arms, which was ridiculous because she knew what a dangerous man he could be. She wanted to feel indifferent to him, but his mere proximity played havoc with her senses as she recalled quite vividly how she had felt when he kissed her. Praying he wasn't reading her thoughts as he sometimes seemed able to do, she tilted her head back, attempting a calm, composed smile.

"Having a nice evening, Kit?" Jason inquired abruptly, his eyes unusually luminescent as they pierced hers. "Or did you just have a little tiff with your boyfriend?"

"Brad's not my boyfriend. Heaven forbid," she protested vehemently. "He's Jess Whitney's brother and the most pious bore you'd ever want to meet."

Jason's narrowed gaze held hers. "If he's such a bore, why are you here with him?"

"Blind date," she confessed, wrinkling her small nose. "I've heard they turn out wonderful once in a while, but this definitely isn't one of those times. Much as I like Jess, I can't say the same for her brother. After making a pass at me, he had the nerve to criticize my father for being a womanizer."

"Why should that bother you? You have the same opinion of Brice, don't you?" Jason asked probingly. "It seems to me you're saying you can criticize your father, but you don't want anyone else to. Is that it?"

Katherine frowned thoughtfully. "Yes, I guess that's it," she admitted at last. "Odd, isn't it? I wonder what it means."

"You know exactly what it means," Jason said flatly, without elaborating. Then, suddenly, lines of strain appeared around his mouth; his arm left her waist and, cupping her elbow, he inclined his head toward the open French doors they had been dancing next to. "Let's walk out on the balcony for a minute."

Katherine went reluctantly, dread mounting in her as she watched his expression grow more grim. Certain he was going to take up yesterday's argument where it had left off, she was tempted to tear free of the hand holding her arm and flee. She was very much afraid she might burst into tears if he hurled any more insults at her. Inexplicably, his opinion of her mattered and she had lain awake most of last night, unable to sleep as the unpleasant remarks they had made to each other reverberated incessantly in her head. Now, she knew there was only one way to avoid renewing the argument tonight. She would have to stop it before it had a chance to even begin.

"About yesterday, Jason," she began, reaching out to touch his forearm with hesitant fingers, then dropping her hand away when he tensed. Hurt more than she should have been by his obvious rejection, she turned to gaze at the lake, its mirror surface shimmering in the light of a full, cream-colored moon. "I just wanted to tell you," she continued finally, "that I know I over-reacted yesterday afternoon and I . . . I said things I really didn't mean."

Jason's hands spanned her waist, turning her back to face him and his answering smile was both mocking and gentle. "Are you saying you suddenly approve of my lifestyle?"

"Well, no, I still don't understand why you want to be a professional gambler, but I'm sure you're right. My lack of understanding stems from my feelings toward my father. But I didn't mean it when I called you a little boy—you don't seem childishly selfish like most other gamblers I've met. So I'm sorry I got all in a huff and said you were a little boy."

"Apology accepted," he murmured, moving closer to her, silhouetted in the shaft of moonlight behind him. "And I must confess I don't consider you a little girl, either."

"Yes, you do," Katherine said unhappily. "You think I act like a child and it irritates you."

He shook his head. "No, it's just that you remind me of my wife."

"Wife?" Katherine gasped weakly, all the strength suddenly draining from her limbs. "You . . . you mean you're married?"

"Was married. I should have said ex-wife," Jason explained calmly. "Since I haven't remarried since we divorced, I guess I still think of her as my wife. And in some ways, Kit, you remind me of her."

This conversation was becoming more dreadfully disturbing with each passing second and Katherine swallowed with difficulty. "You mean I look like her?"

"Not at all. She was tall and dark, nothing like you. But she was young, Kit, and inflexible in her views, maybe even more inflexible than you are. She didn't approve of my . . . profession, thought it was a waste of time. And I had no patience with her when she started in on me so . . . well, suffice it to say, neither of us contested the divorce. We should never have married in the first place. We were both too young."

"And you think I act as young and immature as she did?" Katherine murmured bleakly. "Is that what you're saying?"

"No, not quite. I think you'll probably change, become less inflexible in time, but Denise wasn't capable of change. She's still the same now as she was when we married, as far as I know. Luckily, she found an accountant to marry, who could provide her with a secure, moderately high income, a fashionable house in the suburbs of Denver and very probably the statistically correct two and two-thirds children. So I guess she's as happy now as she ever could be. She feels safe with all those tangible symbols of security."

"I don't think that's the kind of security I want," Katherine defended herself weakly. "I just want some emotional security because . . . well, I guess because my father never provided any."

Jason squeezed her slender waist gently. "I'm beginning to understand that, Kit," he murmured, then brought one hand up to tug at the knot of his dark blue tie. Oddly, his fingers were shaking and as he turned into the light, Katherine could see perspiration beaded on his forehead.

She moved closer to him, intuitively pressing the back of her fingers against his forehead, gasping softly as his skin burned the coolness of hers. "Jason, you're so hot! I think you have a fever. What's wrong? Do you know? Why didn't you tell me you weren't feeling well?"

"It's nothing. At least it's nothing that won't be gone in a few days," he vaguely explained. But when she frowned worriedly up at him, he gave her a weak smile. "Don't give me that Florence Nightingale look, Kit. It's really nothing serious. I picked up this exotic tropical disease in Viet Nam and it recurs occasionally. But the symptoms never last more than a couple of days."

He never ceased surprising her. "I didn't know you were ever in Viet Nam."

"There's a great deal you don't know about me, Kit," he replied. Then, unfastening the top button of his shirt, he shook his head. "I think maybe I should call it a day."

"Of course you should," she chided, concern evident in her voice. "I don't even know why you're here tonight. You should be home in bed. Would you like for me to drive you to your house?"

Shaking his head, he guided her back into the dimly lighted room where they had danced. "No, thanks. You have a date, remember? And I feel well enough to take myself home and put myself to bed after I drive Julie to her apartment."

Julie. The statuesque blonde, no doubt, Katherine thought, jealousy surging through her again. Maybe the gorgeous Julie would even volunteer to go home with him and stay all night. Katherine was certain he wouldn't object. Since he obviously had no desire to accept her own offer to help, there wasn't much else she could do. She inclined her head in a curt nod. "I hope you'll be feeling better tomorrow," she said stiffly. "See you later, I guess." Then, after muttering a hasty good-night, she threaded her way between the dancing couples back to the table where Brad sat glowering as he waited for her.

Three days later, Katherine tiptoed up the stairs to the loft-like second floor in Jason's house where his bedroom was located. In this modified A-frame there were two bedrooms upstairs, a large master suite and a small guest room, both opening into a hall that overlooked the great room. Balancing a tray on one arm, Katherine quietly opened the door, frowning disapprovingly when she caught Jason standing by a bookcase, clad in only a short terry cloth bathrobe.

"What are you doing up?" she asked in her most authoritative voice. "The doctor said you should stay in bed for at least two more days, so get right back in there. If you want a book to read, I'll get it for you."

"You've turned into a real tyrant. You know that, don't you?" he grumbled half-heartedly as he sat down on top of the covers, resting back against the headboard. "I think you enjoy having this chance to boss me around. I suppose you were disappointed when I slept most of the past two days—you couldn't tell me what to do."

"I wasn't here during the day," she countered, setting the tray on the bedside table. "Your housekeeper kept her eye on you then. I just stayed the nights so she could rest. Somebody had to. When I came over here Saturday morning to check on you, you certainly weren't in any condition to be left alone for a moment. But I bet you don't remember that, do you?"

Shaking his head, Jason grinned mischievously. "While I was in such a weakened condition, were you ever tempted to take advantage of me, Kit?"

"Don't be silly," she retorted. When her cheeks colored attractively and he chuckled, she wrinkled her nose at him, then picked up the tray again. "Now, do you feel like eating without my help or would you like me to feed you this soup?"

He groaned, raising his eyes heavenward. "Not that chicken soup again. Come on, Kit, give me a break. Much more of that stuff and I'll start sprouting wings."

"This happens to be beef consomme," she informed him haughtily. "And if you're well enough to wander around your room, you're well enough to feed yourself."

"I was wandering back to bed from taking a shower and shaving. I thought you'd appreciate the fact that I was trying to look devilishly handsome for you," he said mockingly. Unfolding the legs of the lap tray, he set it down and, without warning, reached out and caught her hand in his. "But if you don't sit down and talk to me while I eat this so-called lunch, I'll think I wasted all that effort."

Katherine hesitated, chewing her lower lip. Until today, she hadn't felt self-conscious being here because he had been too feverish to really be aware of her presence. But now that he seemed well on the road to recovery, the circumstances had changed. She was too aware of the intimacy of the situation. Her gaze traveled involuntarily along the muscular length of his legs. Very probably, he had nothing on besides that short terry cloth robe. And they were alone in the house, alone in his *bedroom*. Common sense told her she would be crazy to stay, especially with him in such a provocatively teasing mood. Her free hand fluttered up in a gesture of uncertainty.

"I should go down and straighten the kitchen," she said almost inaudibly. "Your maid's off today so . . ."

"The kitchen can wait. Sit down, Kit," he commanded seriously, his dark eyes holding hers. Dropping her hand, he picked up the spoon and took a cautious sip of the steaming consomme. And when she still remained standing, his dark eyebrows lifted. "Can't you be cooperative for once? Sit down and talk to me while I eat this insipid stuff. Tell me when I can start having something decent to eat."

"Soon," she answered evasively. "Remember the old adage? 'Feed a cold; starve a fever.'"

"I thought that was the other way around."

Grinning at him, she shrugged and sat down. "Well, maybe it is starve a cold and feed a fever. I'm not sure now."

"Some nurse you are," he muttered, sipping another spoonful of the consomme, grimacing as he did so. "Now, seriously, when did the doctor say I could get out of bed?"

"Twenty-four hours after your temperature drops back down to normal." Half-standing, Katherine laid her hand against his forehead. "Umm, you feel much cooler, but I'm sure the doctor will want a thermometer reading to be sure you're not still running a low-grade fever." As she smiled down at him, she suddenly became aware of a certain look in his eyes that made her drop her hand away hastily and subside back on her chair. Avoiding his gaze, she nervously pleated the folds of her yellow combed cotton sundress with her fingers. "So you may be able to get up and move around more tomorrow. Okay? Think you can stand to wait that long?"

Jason smiled sheepishly. "I guess I'm not being a model patient, am I? Sorry, Kit."

She dismissed his apology with a wave of her hand, but her expression was very serious. "When I came here Saturday and realized how sick you were, I wanted to call your family but of course you've never told me anything

78

about them so I couldn't. I don't mean to be nosy, but you do have family somewhere, don't you?"

"My parents and a sister, all in Maine," he said, smiling affectionately. "But I'm glad you couldn't call them. My mother would have gotten all in a dither if she'd known I was sick, even though she realizes this fever recurs every two or three years."

"Do you see them often? Are you close to them?"

"As close as most thirty-three-year-old men are to their families, I suppose," he answered, frowning slightly. "Why all the questions, Kit?"

"I guess I *am* nosy," she admitted, smiling rather shyly. "Or just mystified. You're such a mystery to everybody in Tahoe. No one knows anything about you. Is . . . is there some reason why you don't want them to?"

Jason laughed. "I wasn't aware I was arousing such curiosity. But no, Kit, I'm not hiding some deep, dark secret from my past. I simply don't tell my life history to everybody I meet."

"You're such a strange man," Katherine blurted out indiscreetly, pink color flooding her cheeks as he laughed again. "I mean, I don't know what to expect of you, ever. You're not really the kind of person I assumed you would be. You . . . you confuse me completely."

His lids lowered halfway over his dark blue eyes. "Do I, Kit? I certainly don't mean to." He handed her the tray containing the now empty bowl, his intent gaze following her as she took it and placed it on the table. When she started to sit down again, he caught both her hands in his and drew her down beside him on the edge of the bed. "Tell me how I can make you feel less confused."

"I–I don't know how," she murmured, her pulses pounding frantically in her temples. Unable to look away from him, she searched his lean, brown face for some clue as to what sort of mood he was truly in at that moment.

But since he was a gambler, she supposed he had learned long ago how to disguise his emotions because even as she surveyed him intently, his expression was unreadable. She shifted nervously on the bed's edge, nearly unable to withstand the mesmerizing gaze that captured and held hers. As she realized her fingers ached to entangle in his thick sun-streaked hair, she wondered what was happening to her. It almost seemed as if Jason had become the focal point of her life and it was frightening. No other man had ever permeated her every thought the way he did now. Even in her sleep, when she dreamed, Jason was there and when she awoke every morning, her first conscious thought was of him. It was crazy. She was losing too much of herself to him, especially since his interest in her wasn't in any way serious. Remembering again that she was a fool to be alone in his bedroom with him, she tried to free her hands from his. Her eyes widened with surprise and some fear as his grip on her tightened.

"I have to go," she whispered, shaking her head as he relentlessly pulled her to him. "Jason, please, I should leave."

"Not yet," he whispered back, enfolding her in his arms. "Not quite yet, Kit."

"But you're ill," she protested, holding herself stiffly against his chest. "You need to rest."

"I'd rather do this," he murmured, his breath stirring a tendril of auburn-gold hair across her temple. He removed the ribbon that secured her braid, combing his long, lean fingers through the gently waving strands. "Your hair's so soft, like pure silk."

"Jason." She sighed, reluctantly relaxing against him as his strong fingers grazed her nape, melting all resistance. He lowered her to the bed, moving with her, pressing her slender body beneath the comforting weight of his. Lost in the fiery blue depths of his eyes, Katherine lifted her arms around his shoulders, concealing her own eyes beneath the

thick fringe of her long lashes. With a sharply indrawn breath, she felt his lips seek the warm hollow at the base of her throat, then graze upward to her wildly beating pulse.

Her small, trembling fingers feathered over the tendons of his neck and she found delight in the ragged tenor of his breathing that accompanied her tentative, inexperienced caress. Her eyes closed completely. The world swirled around her. As he lowered the straps of her dress, baring her shoulders to his light teasing kisses, she trembled as a burning desire threatened to consume her. Lost in the pleasurable sensations his touch evoked, she wanted nothing more than to stay in his bed with him forever. Beyond thought, she slipped her hands beneath the lapels of his robe, her nails catching in the fine dark hair matting his chest.

Whispering her name, Jason lifted his head, catching her small chin between his thumb and forefinger. A slight pressure exerted by his thumb was all that was needed to entice her lips apart and the eagerness conveyed by her tender bow-shaped mouth was more than he could resist. His lips descended violently, their hard searching strength ravishing the softly textured warmth of hers.

Delight raced through her. She arched her slender body against him. Beneath his robe, her searching hands feathered across his lean sides, then linked tightly over his broad, powerful back, urging him closer. His knee pressed between hers and as their legs tangled, he wound the tousled thickness of her hair around his hand, tilting her head back as he blazed a fiery trail of kisses along the creamy length of her slender neck.

"I can't leave you alone," he muttered huskily in her ear. "I've tried, but I just can't." He turned over onto his side, taking her with him. He slowly lowered the zipper of her dress and with swift expertise draped it down around her hips. His fingers brushed aside the swirling hair that cascaded down to cover her breasts.

She felt his burning gaze on her bared skin. Opening drowsy eyes, she watched his brown fingers stroke her alabaster breasts, moving slowly up the full throbbing roundness to trace exquisite circles around the aroused rose-tinted peaks. Anticipation mounted unbearably as he slowly lowered his head. His mouth sought first one satin-textured tip, then the other, his teeth nibbling gently until her senses were swimming and she was aching for the satisfaction of total surrender.

She explored the contours of his ears, his neck, his corded shoulders with trembling fingers as the tip of his tongue, brushing with moist warmth over her taut, surging nipples, created wild pulsating waves that rippled deep within her, less frightening than they were irresistible. Yet even as she never wanted to lose the touch of his lips on forbidden skin, she needed his mouth against hers again. Tangling her fingers in his thick vital hair, she urged him to lift his head. "Kiss me." She sighed softly and as he did, she wrapped her arms around his neck, matching his passion as she strained against the powerful length of his lean, aroused body.

Muttering a hoarse exclamation against her clinging tender lips, he dragged her hands from round his neck, guiding them down to the belt of his robe. "Untie it," he commanded ardently. "Please, Kit, let me love you."

This time, it was his careless use of the word "love" that brought her to her senses. He didn't love her, the remnants of her common sense screamed at her. But she was beginning to fall in love with him and if she allowed him to use her to assuage his purely physical needs, she knew she would be irrevocably hurt when he tired of her in the near future. The instinct for self-preservation suddenly overpowered the dizzying effects of his expert lovemaking. Fear exploded in her, the fear that she might have waited too late to be able to stop him. Inciting herself to panic, she struggled frantically beneath him, pushing at his hard muscular chest, begging, "Jason, I can't. I just can't go through with it. Please don't make me. Please."

He tensed, then with a muffled groan, rolled over onto his back, covering his eyes with his forearm.

As his breathing began to slow to a normal rate, her trembling ceased and in the debilitating silence, a dull heaviness settled on her. She was awaiting some word from him, but finally she could bear the ominous quiet in the room no longer. Foolishly, she laid her hand against his chest, murmuring, "I'm sorry. I . . ."

"No . . . don't touch me again," he commanded roughly, pushing her hand away. "And get off the bed before I decide to make love to you, with or without your consent."

She knew he meant it. She slipped hastily off the bed, dragging the straps of her dress back up over her shoulders, then reached behind her back to pull up the zipper. For a moment, she stared miserably at him, wondering how angry he was. He had every right to be furious. Leading him on, then saying no at the last minute had been despicable and she wasn't at all proud of herself. She took one step toward the bed, then hesitated, not knowing what she could say to him, almost relieved when he saved her the trouble by speaking first.

"Kit," he said tiredly, propping himself up on his elbows to look broodingly at her. "Go home."

She shook her head obstinately. "I won't. You need me to look after you."

"I'm much better now. I can take care of myself."

Breathing a sigh, she went to him, touching his forehead with the back of her hand. "Your temperature's up again."

He laughed humorlessly catching her hand and putting it away from him. "Any man's temperature would be up after what just happened here."

Massaging her temples, she gazed at him imploringly.

"I'm sorry. I don't know what's wrong with me lately. I just . . ."

"You're just young, Kit, too young and inexperienced for me. I wouldn't want to rush you into a relationship you're not ready for so . . ." He smiled indulgently at the pink color that suffused her cheeks. "I think you should go home now."

Nodding, she turned and walked to the door, halting before she stepped out into the hallway. "I'll be back to stay with you tonight, though."

"No!" he said harshly, relenting when her green eyes darkened unhappily. "No, don't come tonight, Kit. It wouldn't be wise for you to."

"But you're still not well and I am coming, about eight," she informed him stubbornly, then rushed away before he could force her to change her mind.

Jason wasn't a man to be easily defied, however, as Katherine learned that evening after dinner. As she was helping Mallie with the dishes, the phone rang. The housekeeper answered, then handed the receiver to Katherine. It was Jason.

"It won't be necessary for you to come tonight," he said flatly. "Someone else will stay here with me."

Katherine didn't believe him for a minute. "You're just saying that because you don't think I *should* come."

"I don't imagine your father thinks it's a very good idea, either," Jason muttered, his tone weary. "So just stay home, Kit. I do have someone to spend the night here."

"Who?" she challenged. "If someone's staying, you shouldn't mind telling me who it is."

There was a long pause, then Jason muttered rather reluctantly. "It's Julie; she'll be here all night."

Katherine felt as if a brick had been hurled against her chest. The intense, biting pain radiated through her, but she was determined not to give him any indication of the hurt he had inflicted. "Julie. That's the blond woman you were with at the restaurant," she stated flatly, then added in a suggestive tone, "Well, I'm sure she'll take *very* good care of you."

"No doubt," was his unabashed answer.

After whispering a rushed good-bye, Katherine replaced the receiver of the yellow wall phone, then stood immobile, staring at the floor.

"Anything the matter, honey?" Mallie asked gently. "You look mighty pale. Not bad news, I hope?"

"News I should have expected," Katherine answered cryptically, then hurried out of the kitchen, down the hall to her bedroom where she locked her door behind her. If she had needed proof that she meant nothing to Jason, his rejection of her tonight had certainly been it. "You should have known that all along, you nitwit," she muttered aloud as she flung herself across her bed. And though the pressure of tears she needed to shed built steadily behind her eyes, she refused to cry.

Chapter Six

A week later, Katherine was at the casino, having been drafted into service as a cocktail waitress again. This time, however, since she was needed from three in the afternoon until midnight, her father wanted her to wear a skimpy little black satin uniform. Eyeing herself in the mirror in the locker room, Katherine chewed her upper lip. She could hardly believe her own father wanted her to wear this. The rounded, besequined neckline plunged down to expose a generous portion of her full, uplifted breasts and the short, circular skirt barely grazed the tops of her thighs. She felt positively indecent though in actuality, she had more on now than she did when she wore her bikini. Yet, it was the principle of the matter or maybe her reluctance to parade around the casino in such scanty attire stemming from the fact that she had noticed Jason's silver Jaguar in the parking lot when she had driven in.

For some reason, she didn't want him to see her in this

diminutive uniform though, to her embarrassment, he had seen her in less. Even so, to trot around him *and* all the other men in the casino would be humiliating, she was sure. She would be afraid he was seeing her as the rest of them did, as a fairly attractive body, scantily clad for their entertainment. She wanted to be more to Jason than a body he wanted to touch and possess. But she also knew that merely wanting that wouldn't make it true. Sighing heavily, she examined her reflection critically, then on impulse brought her hair forward over each shoulder so the long cascading tresses concealed the creamy skin of her bosom. There, that was better, she decided, smiling wryly, glad she hadn't cut her hair short as she had considered doing last year. At least, with it waist-long, she had something to hide behind.

Finally, she realized she could dawdle in the locker room no longer. Gathering up her courage, she ventured out onto the casino floor, feeling more than a little self-conscious as she started toward the bar. Her father stopped her between the keno and baccarat tables. After giving her one of his nervous little smiles, he looked her over carefully, then frowned. "You have pretty hair, Kit, but I don't think you need to wear it like a cloak," he criticized gently. Yet, when he lifted the waving auburn strands back over her shoulders, a startled expression flitted across his usually immobile features. "I didn't realize you'd . . . uh . . . filled out so much in the past year," he muttered uncomfortably, without meeting her eyes. "You don't look so much like a little girl anymore, Kit; you look more like a woman." A less objective survey of her followed as his eyes swept over her from head to toe. Then, amazingly, he drew her hair forward again, over her shoulders. "Maybe you were right; it suits you better this way."

As he walked away from her then, she stared after him, quite surprised that he had changed his mind. It actually seemed as if he were beginning to experience some paternal emotions toward her. First, he had warned her away from Jason, as if he feared for her innocence, and now he seemed to be saying he didn't want a bunch of strange men ogling his daughter's body. For the first time in her life, she really felt she had a father and it was such a poignant emotion that tears sprang to her eyes. Blinking them away, she went on to the bar to ask which section of the casino she had been assigned to serve.

Three hours later, Katherine was sent with a tray of drinks to one of the private rooms. Pausing before a full-length gilt edged mirror in the hallway, she grimaced disgustedly at the bruise that was developing on her right thigh. One very inebriated blackjack player had decided he had every right to manhandle her and before she could sidestep him, he had pinched her enthusiastically. It had taken all the self-control she could muster not to send him sprawling with a resounding slap, but she had held her anger in check and simply moved beyond his reach. Wishing she were on the beach by the lake, she went on to quietly open the door to the room where the private poker game was going on.

Her eyes were drawn immediately to Jason. Cool and composed as ever, he was sliding a stack of chips toward the center of the table, saying flatly, "See your thousand and raise you two." The man next to him uttered an explicit curse as he tossed his entire hand on the table. "Fold," he muttered irritably, watching Jason rake in all the chips from the center. Though he had obviously won a big pot, his expression didn't change one whit. The blue eyes that Katherine had seen ablaze with passion were cool and emotionless now. Yet, when he glanced up and saw her, a sudden light flickered in the azure depths. With a careless wave of his hand, he stood. "Deal me out this time."

Katherine cursed her racing heart and took an involuntary step backward as Jason came to where she stood by the door. His narrowed gaze drifted slowly over her, from flaming auburn hair to trim ankles and small slender feet ensconced in black satin high-heel shoes.

"You don't look so young to me now, Miss Delacorte," he murmured so only she could hear. Then as warm color rose in her cheeks, he laughed softly. "On second thought, you do."

"You're impossible," she muttered nervously. "You treat me like I'm thirteen."

"In sexual experience, you are about thirteen."

"Not since I met you," she retorted, an unwittingly provocative luminosity in her eyes. "You've given me a crash course."

"But you still haven't taken the final exam," he responded seriously, his teasing smile fading. "So you still have to consider yourself inexperienced. And I have to remember to consider that, too."

"Why? You haven't seen me in a week so I don't imagine you've thought of me in any way at all," she replied tautly, trying to conceal her resentment. But it was revealed all too clearly in her flashing eyes. "In other words: Out of sight, out of mind."

A muscle ticked in Jason's jaw and he moved closer, almost menacingly. "You wouldn't want that final exam before you're really ready for it, would you? If not, then it's probably wiser for us not to see each other."

"If that's the way you want it," she murmured, gazing down at his feet, veiling with the fringe of her lashes the pain she was certain must be mirrored in her eyes. Without looking up, she sidestepped him. "I'd better serve these drinks. Excuse me."

As she approached the table, the irritable man who had lost to Jason glared past Katherine at the younger man. "You going to proposition the girl or play poker, Roarke? We'd like a chance to win back some of our money."

"Deal me in," Jason replied calmly, going to take his seat again.

After serving the drinks and pouring a cup of coffee for Jason, Katherine escaped the room as quickly as possible without looking directly at him again. Unfortunately, that disturbing encounter was only a prelude to another. In the hall leading back to the casino, she met Julie, Jason's satuesque blond friend. Eyeing the empty tray Katherine carried, the older girl halted her with an upraised hand, inclining her head toward the closed door to the private room.

"How's it going in there?" she asked. "Jason winning again?"

"I think he is," Katherine answered flatly, dismayed to see that Julie was lovelier close up than she was at a distance. With warm brown eyes, platinum hair that was disgustingly natural, and a curvaceous figure, she looked like a Greek goddess. Katherine suddenly understood perfectly why Jason was no longer interested in seeing her anymore. With a woman like Julie at his beck and call, he certainly wouldn't want to waste his time on a twenty-one-year-old girl, too inhibited to give him what he needed. Resignation settled heavily in Katherine and she was unable even to force a wan smile at the taller girl. She shrugged instead. "Of course, since I know very little about poker, he could just as easily be losing, as far as I know."

"Jason rarely loses," Julie said smugly, as if she were taking credit for his success. "But you should know that. You're a friend of his, aren't you? Didn't I see him talking to you in the restaurant at Harrah's the other night?"

"Jason and I know each other," Katherine answered shortly, her tone implying she had no desire to elaborate. "Casual acquaintances, I guess you might say."

Julie giggled rather sillily. "Well, you're a little too young to be anything but a casual acquaintance." She inspected Katherine thoroughly, then frowned. "In fact, you look too young to be a cocktail waitress. What did you do? Lie to the boss and tell him you were older?"

Tiring of the inquisition, beginning to lose her patience, Katherine silently counted to ten before saying, "The boss happens to be my father and since I'm only filling in *without* pay for one of the waitresses who's out, it doesn't matter how old I am."

"Oh, you're Brice's little girl!" Julie enthused, smiling condescendingly. "Well, it's a small world, isn't it, honey? Brice and I are old friends. He got me my first job here two years ago, as a dancer in the revue. We were very close for a while back then but . . . Oh, well, you know how it goes." She shrugged carelessly. "But still, I'm surprised Brice lets you fill in as a cocktail waitress. You can't be more than eighteen."

"I'm twenty-one," Katherine informed her, thrusting out her small chin. "And my father seems to think that's old enough."

"Well, maybe it's that long hair of yours that makes you look so much younger," Julie said, casting a faintly disparaging glance at the cascading auburn tresses. "If you cut it short or even wore it swept up, you'd probably look more your age. And with a little eye shadow and more mascara, you'd . . ."

"I'll keep your advice in mind," Katherine interrupted, wishing Julie would just be quiet and let her go on her way. Waving the empty tray hintingly, she added, "I imagine they're short-handed without me so I'd better get back to work."

"Sure, go ahead. I have to go too. I promised Jason I'd look in on his game before I had to start rehearsal. He says I bring him luck." Julie smiled suggestively, then lifted a limp hand in a wave. "See you around, kid. Okay?"

Not if I see you coming first, Katherine thought impatiently, though she nodded before turning away. As she marched down the hall, a grim smile appeared on her lips. She hoped Julie brought Jason rotten luck this evening. In fact, she hoped he lost every dime he had. Knowing that was highly unlikely, however, Katherine allowed her shoulders to sag. Jealousy built in her, turning her distaste for Julie into an emotion more akin to hatred. But, though she wanted to direct some of her intense animosity toward Jason, she was too realistic to try to deceive herself. What she felt for him was most assuredly not hate.

The day went from bad to worse. Less than two hours after Katherine's chat with Julie, she heard someone calling her name from across the casino. When she turned, she saw the aspiring singer she had met on the plane, Wendi Miller, beckoning to her excitedly. Having just delivered a trayful of drinks to the keno table, Katherine had no excuse to delay saying hello to Wendi. But the speculative gleam in the petite girl's eyes wasn't exactly encouraging as she walked across the crowded casino.

"I'll have you know I've been looking for you for the past five days," Wendi began almost irritably as soon as Katherine reached her. "I was beginning to think you'd fallen in the lake and drowned. Where have you been keeping yourself anyway? I've been in here every afternoon and evening, hoping I'd see you."

"I don't come to the casino any more than I have to," Katherine replied honestly. "The only reason I'm here today is because three of the cocktail waitresses are out sick with a virus. So my father drafted me."

Wendi's eyes lighted up when Katherine mentioned her father. "Didn't you tell me your old man manages this place?" she asked unnecessarily, feigning an uncertain frown. "Or was it somebody else I met whose father works at one of the ritzier hotels?"

"My father doesn't manage the hotel, just the casino."

Hoping to avoid what she knew was coming next, Katherine started to walk away. "Well, I have to get busy."

"But wait!" Wendi cried, catching her arm none too gently. "Now would be the perfect time for me to meet your father. Remember, when we talked on the plane, you promised to introduce me to him."

Katherine shook her head. "I don't recall promising that."

"Well, you did," Wendi lied outright, her delicate facial features hardening as she adjusted the barely decent bodice of her flashy orange print sundress. "You said if I was ever anywhere around Cedars, to look you up and you would introduce me to him."

Wendi had said on the plane she was willing to do anything to get a singing engagement and Katherine had believed her. For that reason, she wasn't eager to have the girl meet Brice, so she shook her head again. "Now's not a good time, Wendi, sorry. I'm sure my father's too busy to meet anyone."

Tears that didn't seem quite genuine filled Wendi's eyes and her lips trembled. "Oh, please, Kathy. I'm desperate. None of the hotels are hiring, so I haven't been able to see anybody with any authority since I've been here. I get turned away by secretaries before I even get a chance to audition." She sniffled. "You're the last hope I've got. I don't know anybody else here and since your father probably knows the very people I need to meet, couldn't you please just introduce me to him? Oh, please. If you'd just do that much for me, I'd be grateful forever."

Katherine sighed. As on the first day they had met, she felt a surge of pity for the older girl. "Look, Wendi," she said gently. "It's just so hard to get a job here as a singer or a dancer. So many people audition and so many of them are really good."

"But I'm really good, too," the girl insisted, clutching

Katherine's arm. "I really am. If you could just hear me . . ."

"I don't doubt you're a very good singer," Katherine assured her kindly. "But as far as I know they have all the singers they need in both the lounges here and most of the big-name talents bring their own back-up groups. I wish I could be more encouraging, but it's just so hard to get a break in a gambling resort town. Maybe you should go somewhere like Los Angeles or something and get a better agent."

"I can't go anywhere! I only have enough money to stay here a couple more nights!" Wendi cried. "After that's gone, who knows what I'll have to do to survive."

Now, Katherine didn't know what to say. Though Wendi should have had the common sense to have saved enough money to leave here, she hadn't done so and Katherine could sympathize with her plight. Yet, she still didn't want to introduce the girl to her father and she shifted her feet uncomfortably, trying to decide what to do.

The decision was made for her. "Taking a break, Kit?" Brice asked as he stepped behind her and as she turned, he gave her a half smile. Then he noticed Wendi, who had turned on a deliberately seductive smile. His solemn green eyes swept over her dark hair and petite yet curvaceous figure, narrowing appraisingly. After a long moment, he turned back to his daughter. "Well, if you're taking a break, you might as well do it in comfort. Come on to the office. And bring your friend along."

Katherine was trapped. As Brice strode away, she had no choice but to follow and Wendi was nearly skipping along side her. "Ooh, isn't this just perfect. He is your father, isn't he? He must be. You have eyes just like his. And he's not busy after all. You can introduce me to him."

Katherine nodded reluctantly, her stomach muscles tensing. Some sixth sense told her she would regret making this introduction for a long time. Unless she wanted Wendi to cause a scene, however, she lacked any other alternative. Dragging her feet, she followed her father through the receptionist's office, sighing as Wendi nearly stumbled over her in her eagerness to keep up with him. Then as Brice opened the door to his secretary's office and Katherine saw Jess look up from her desk and smile fondly at him, she had to bite back the groan that rose in her throat. If her father became involved with the irrepressible Wendi, Jess was going to be hurt once again and, indirectly, it would be all Katherine's fault or at least she felt that it would. What a stupid mess, she thought miserably, tempted for a moment to leave before she could make the introduction. But it was too late. Her father and Wendi were already exchanging interested glances and the smile on Jess's face had been replaced by an expression of weary resignation. So when Brice looked at his daughter expectantly, she simply did what she had to do. She introduced him to Wendi, who languidly held out to him the hand that bore a ring on every finger. He held it longer than necessary, his gaze drifting over her voluptuous body again, then he gave her one of his enigmatic smiles. "You like jewelry, Miss Miller?"

Wendi laughed coyly. "I'm like most other women, Mr. Delacorte. I like nice things."

"Call me Brice," Katherine's father said, finally releasing the beringed hand. "And what do you do to earn money so you can buy yourself nice things?"

"Oh, I'm a singer, a very good one. In fact, I've sung in some of the best clubs in San Francisco," Wendi said, embellishing the truth as she had told it to Katherine on the plane. "Right now, I'm on vacation. I came to Tahoe to see if I might like to work here. I've decided it's a pretty nice place. And since Kathy . . . I mean, Kit, and I became friends on the plane, she offered to ask you if you might have some contacts in the bigger hotels." She laughed too brightly. "So, I decided I'd drop by and meet you. She said she was sure you wouldn't mind."

Brice ignored Katherine's sharp intake of breath. Though he couldn't have possibly believed Wendi's lies, it didn't seem to matter if what she'd said wasn't true. "I do know a few people," he said softly, cupping the girl's elbow. "So why don't we go into my office and discuss this."

Giving him another provocative smile, Wendi moved close against his side, glancing up at him with genuine interest in her eyes. Brice's silent, brooding, yet commanding personality obviously intrigued her as it had intrigued countless young women before her. Without so much as a good-bye to Katherine, Wendi allowed Brice to escort her inside his private office.

The moment the door closed behind them, Katherine spun around to face Jess. "I didn't offer to introduce her to him, honestly, Jess," she said urgently, regret darkening her eyes to deep green pools. "I wouldn't ever have volunteered to bring a girl like her here to meet him. She's desperate to find a job in one of the lounges so I knew what she'd be willing to do if she met Father. I would never have brought her here willingly because I wouldn't hurt you for anything, Jess. Please believe me. I just met her again out in the casino, then my father came along and . . ."

"Hush, Kit," Jess said softly, with an understanding smile. "It's all right. If it hadn't been her, it would have been some other young woman just like her, so don't blame yourself."

"How do you stand it, Jess?" Katherine whispered miserably, thinking as much of Jason and Julie as she was of Wendi and Brice. "Doesn't it hurt you terribly to see him with someone else?"

"It hurts, but not as much as it did at first," Jess

answered, staring pensively at her desk. "Or maybe I'm just used to it after all this time."

Not long ago, Katherine would have asked Jess why she didn't just walk out on Brice, but since she had met Jason, Katherine was beginning to realize some problems simply didn't have easy solutions. How odd it was. After seeing how her father had hurt Jess, she herself had gotten too involved with a man just like him.

On impulse, she went around the desk to brush a kiss across Jess's cheek. "I wish you could have fallen in love with someone more dependable ten years ago," she said softly. "But I guess we don't always love wisely, do we?"

As Jess shook her head, Katherine went to the window to stare out, not really noticing the boughs of the tall pines and shorter, fuller cedars swaying in the breeze. She sighed. Then a sharp, unrelenting pain settled in her chest as she looked at the parking lot and saw Jason and Julie standing beside the silver Jaguar. As she watched, the blonde stretched up on tiptoe to press her lips against his in a lingering kiss. Hastily turning from the window, Katherine bit down hard on her lower lip. "You know," she said tremulously, "I feel very out of place here."

Jess looked up, her smile too wise. "I know exactly what you mean, Kit," she murmured sympathetically. "You wouldn't believe how many times I've thought the very same thing about myself."

Chapter Seven

Katherine arose later than usual the next morning, having spent a restless night. Dragging herself out of bed reluctantly, she shed her white cotton nightgown and went to take a bracing shower, hoping it would make her feel a bit more energetic. The cool spray bouncing against her skin succeeded in making her feel more alert and after putting on a sleeveless, cream-colored sundress that accentuated her light tan, she sat down before the vanity mirror to arrange her hair in a loose chignon on her nape.

Deciding she looked too pale, she applied a light amount of peach-tinted blusher to her cheeks, then brushed mascara onto the sun-bleached tips of her brown lashes. Leaning closer to the mirror, she examined the faint shadows beneath her eyes. If Mallie noticed them, Katherine supposed she could explain them away by lying and saying she had read too late last night. Actually, though, she had fallen asleep almost immediately after going to bed, only to awaken after a couple of hours and lie there until nearly dawn's first light, thinking of Jason.

"Stupid waste of time," she told her reflection with a disparaging toss of her hand. "I just bet he didn't waste his night thinking about you when he had Julie to keep him entertained."

Julie. The mere thought of the dancer was enough to increase the tight ache in Katherine's chest. Her father had told her that Jason had been out with a couple of the showgirls but didn't seem involved with anyone in particular. Now it looked as if that had changed. He and Julie were apparently seeing each other quite often so Katherine had no choice except to assume their relationship was becoming serious. Of course, she had suspected Jason didn't spend all his nights alone, but it hadn't hurt so much to think of him with women who meant nothing to him. But apparently, Julie was different. He had even asked her to come stay with him when he was sick, making it quite clear that she meant more to him than Katherine did.

That hurt much more than Katherine knew she should allow it to. From the beginning, she had known what kind of life he led, that he made no lasting commitments, and she had resolved not to become involved with him for those very reasons. Now that her firm resolution had crumbled to dust, she could blame no one except herself for the emotional wreck she was becoming.

"Oh, drat," she muttered, irritated at Jason and at herself and at the whole world in general.

After making her bed, Katherine left her room to go into the kitchen for a much needed cup of coffee. Her father was already there, seated at the table in the breakfast nook. When she walked in, he laid his newspaper aside to half smile at her.

"You're late getting up this morning," he commented as she sat down across from him, cupping a mug of coffee in her small, slender hands. "You're feeling all right, aren't you?"

"Fine," she answered shortly, still miffed at him because of his reaction when he met Wendi last night. Through the fringe of her lowered lashes, Katherine eyed him speculatively. Actually, she wouldn't have been surprised if he had not come home last night at all. She suspected Wendi Miller would have gladly welcomed him to spend the night in her hotel room, despite the fact that she had only known him a few hours.

Since he was home, though, Katherine's attitude mellowed slightly. At least he hadn't been completely taken in by Wendi's batting eyelashes and sugary, come-hither smile.

"Didn't you say you planned to go shopping early this morning?" Brice questioned further, reaching into the inside pocket of his jacket. He brought out a slim, expensive Moroccan leather wallet, from which he withdrew several bills of large denomination. "Of course, I want you to charge all your school clothes to me as usual, but this is mad money. Go to a jewelry store, perhaps; buy something really nice." He held out the money, smiling that crooked, rather uncomfortable smile.

After hesitating for a moment, Katherine took the money, staring at the sheaf of twenty-dollar bills. "But there's over two hundred dollars here," she exclaimed softly, confusion unmistakable in her green eyes as she looked back up at him. "It's too much. You're paying for all my school clothes anyway. So you don't have to give me this, too."

"I know I don't have to. I want to," he said flatly, his tone discouraging further argument. "Just spend it, Kit. Buy yourself a pretty gold chain or something. Now, since it usually takes you all day to shop for clothes, I think you should get going. Don't you?"

"I guess so," she agreed, smiling her thanks. But as she

folded the money and slipped it into her dress pocket, she heard footsteps in the hall and the door open behind her. As she turned to greet Mallie, her eyes widened and she had to bite back a surprised exclamation. It wasn't Mallie who sauntered lazily into the kitchen. It was Wendi Miller, acting as if she had every right to wander unannounced into Brice's house. Ignoring Katherine, she gave him a languorous and too familiar smile.

"Morning, darling," she whispered seductively, leaning down to kiss his cheek. "How do you manage to look so well rested and alert? You didn't leave me until after three this morning and I must admit I feel so lazy, I think I could sleep 'til noon. But since you promised to introduce me to the fellow who books the entertainment at Cedars, I decided to come over here and ride to the hotel with you."

Resentment erupted in Katherine and she turned a chilling glare on her father, her eyes glittering like shards of green ice. To his credit, he did seem embarrassed, but Katherine was so disgusted with him at that moment, she hardly realized she was seeing him blush for the first time in her life. Clenching her jaw, she rose to her feet, tossed her napkin down on the table, then marched out of the kitchen without so much as a glance at Wendi.

In the hall, Katherine's hands balled into tight fists at her sides. She could hardly believe her father was actually becoming involved with an obvious gold digger like Wendi Miller. This was too much. It had been difficult enough to respect him before. Now, Katherine was certain she could never look him straight in the eye again. Storming into her room, she slammed the door behind her, not caring if the sound reverberated throughout the house. She kicked off her cork-soled sandals, gaining some grim satisfaction as one went soaring through the air to land with a resounding thump on the cedar hope chest. She was muttering to herself as her door was suddenly opened and she spun around just when Brice stepped into her room.

"Kit, I think we should discuss this. I . . ."

"I don't want to talk to you," she announced stiltedly. "There's absolutely nothing to say."

"Yes, there is," he argued, approaching her. He sighed when he reached out as if to touch her hair and she jerked away. "Kit, listen, I can explain."

"You don't need to explain," she muttered rather sarcastically. "I have eyes and what I just saw explains everything to me."

"Be reasonable, for heaven's sake," he mumbled, beginning to pace back and forth in front of her, avoiding her accusing stare. "I may be your father, Kit, but I'm also a man. And you're old enough to understand now that men have certain needs."

Too angry to blush, Katherine only grimaced distastefully. "I do understand that. But must you satisfy these 'certain' needs with . . . with women like *her?* For goodness sake, she's so . . . so *willing.* And not just with you, I'm sure. So your involvement with her had to be meaningless. Isn't it? Isn't it utterly meaningless?"

His pacing ceased as he stared broodingly at her. "Look, Kit, I didn't expect you to ever know I was seeing her. I had no idea she would drop by here this morning. I'm sorry she did while you were still here."

"Why?" Katherine countered sharply, staring right back at him. "If I hadn't seen her this morning, would your relationship with her seem more proper to you? Or would it just have been easier for you to keep seeing her on the sly? If you feel the need to sneak around, you must know you're crazy to be involved with her! You must realize she expects something out of all this. She's using you! You must know that."

"I know that very well," Brice responded curtly, his own green eyes taking on an impatient glitter. "I'm no fool."

"Then why do you continually get yourself involved with women like Wendi?" Katherine retorted heatedly. "What's the matter with you? There's Jess . . ."

"What the devil does Jess have to do with any of this?" Brice interrupted irritably. "Why drag her name into it?"

"If you don't know why, then I'm certainly not going to tell you," Katherine answered disgustedly. "Just tell me why you let women like Wendi use you? All she wants is a singing engagement somewhere here in Tahoe and she's hoping you'll use your influence to get her one."

"I'm well aware of that. I certainly didn't think she'd fallen madly in love with me. Nor would I want her to. Look, Kit, Wendi and I are both adults. We're attracted to each other."

"I suppose that means you plan to go on seeing her?" Katherine exclaimed disbelievingly. "Although you admit she's only using you, you plan to see her again? You can't be serious! But you are, aren't you? Well, let me tell you something: If you keep seeing her, you won't be seeing me. I'll leave here and that's a promise."

Brice muttered a curse beneath his breath. "You seem to be forgetting that I'm the parent here. You're the child and I'm the father," he proclaimed brusquely, with more emotion than his daughter had ever seen him display. "You may be twenty-one, young lady, but you'll not begin to tell me what to do."

Katherine gasped softly. Her father had never spoken to her that way before. He sounded like . . . like a *father* and it was a little too late. After years of paying little attention to her, she deeply resented his exercising his parental prerogative now. Even though he was her father, he certainly couldn't order her to live with him while he and his . . . his *doxy* conducted their shabby fleeting affair. She simply wouldn't do it. Squaring her shoulders, she stared defiantly at him. "All right, keep seeing her, but don't expect me to stick around here, condoning this meaningless relationship. I won't live under the same roof with you as long as you're involved with her!"

"Katherine," he muttered, his use of her proper name a warning in itself. "I've heard enough from you this morning." Reaching into his trouser pocket, he withdrew his keys. "Now, take the Porsche and go shopping as you planned. And forget all this. It doesn't concern you."

"You think not?" she asked mockingly, pulling the money he had given her from her dress pocket. "Well, I think it concerns me plenty and I'm not about to let you ease your guilty conscience by sending me on a shopping spree. Here, take your two hundred and give it to Wendi. She earned it, I'm sure. And don't think I'll buy clothes for school, either. I'd walk around campus naked before I'd take anything from you."

"You're over-reacting," her father said succinctly, ignoring the money she thrust out toward him. He went to the door, then stopped to look back at her. "After you've calmed down, we'll discuss your school clothes again. Now, I'm late so . . ."

As he left the room, Katherine flung the bills down as hard as she could, turning away before they could flutter to the floor. She muttered a muffled imprecation. So he thought he could force her to stay here with him while he allowed that bimbo to use him. Well, she'd show him. She didn't quite know how but she would.

Katherine spent the rest of the day at the lake, alternately sitting on the beach plotting revenge and swimming vigorously to expend nervous energy. For a while, she considered flying home to Baltimore immediately, then discarded that method of making her father sorry for what he was doing. Leaving wasn't the answer; that would make it too easy for him to continue living the way he did. She wanted to do something that would really make him sit up and take notice, something that would force him to reevaluate his own lifestyle. And at about four in the afternoon, the perfect idea hit Katherine like a bolt of lightning out of the blue. She laughed gleefully. She would fix him. Giving him back a little of his own medicine was the perfect solution.

After gathering up her beach paraphernalia, Katherine rushed back to the house and when she had washed her hair in the shower and toweled it partially dry, she took a suitcase from her closet and began to pack. When she had put in the clothing she thought she'd need, she placed her small collection of cosmetics into a zippered plastic-lined bag, then tucked it in a pocket of the suitcase. Then as she added an extra pair of shoes she thought she might need, Mallie knocked once on her door and came into the room.

Seeing the suitcase, the housekeeper frowned. "What are you up to?" she asked sharply. "You can't be meaning to leave?"

"That's exactly what I'm meaning to do," Katherine answered calmly, discarding her cotton robe to don denim cut-off shorts and a denim halter top. "And I'm sure you know why I'm leaving."

"I know you're upset with your daddy for bringing that no-account woman here and I ain't blaming you for feeling that way," Mallie said with a disapproving grunt. "I ain't never liked it for Mr. Brice to carry on with such women and I think it was mighty bad of him to take up with a new one while you're here. But I reckon he thinks you're grown up enough to accept his ways."

Katherine tossed her hand in an impatient gesture. "Well, I don't accept them and I never will."

"Good. But I still don't see how you're going to help things by running back home to your mama."

"But I'm not running back home to Mother, Mallie," Katherine said as she closed her suitcase. Then she looked up at the housekeeper, giving her a gentle smile. "Now, don't get upset when I tell you this. I plan to teach my father a lesson by moving in with a man."

Mallie nearly choked on a gasp and turned so red that Katherine had to pound her back before she could catch her breath. Then righteous indignation shook her entire body and her double chin trembled as she glared at Katherine imperiously. "You'll do no such thing, young lady. I never heard such talk in my life! Move in with a man, my foot! You'll not do it, if I have to sit on you to keep you here."

"You can't stop me, Mallie, my mind's made up," Katherine said flatly, going to take her suitcase off her bed. "If my father can bring Wendi into this house to stay, then I can go live with a man if I want to. I'm twenty-one. He can't stop me and neither can you."

Mallie changed her tactics. "But honey," she said cajolingly, "you can't do something so foolish. You're a good girl, just an innocent. You could get yourself in a heap of trouble, trying to pick up some man to move in with."

Katherine shook her head. "I don't plan to pick up anybody. I don't have to. I already have a particular man in mind."

"Who?" Mallie questioned suspiciously. "Not that bigtime gambler, Roarke, or whatever his name is? The one you fretted so much over when he was sick?"

"That's the one," Katherine said airily. "But don't worry about me, Mallie. Jason has an extra bedroom in his house. And I just plan to stay long enough to give my father something to think about. As soon as he stops seeing Wendi, I'll come back again."

Mallie shook her head incredulously. "You really think a man like this Roarke fellow is going to let you move in with him and not expect something back from you? Kit, he's a man, ain't he?"

"He's not quite the ruthless wastrel you might think," Katherine found herself defending him. "If I explain why I want to stay at his house for a few days, I'm sure he'll cooperate without expecting . . . expecting, well, you know . . ."

"All I know is that man means something to you, child," Mallie said quietly, examining Katherine's face with keen perception. "I could see it in your eyes when he was sick. And if you think you're falling in love with him, it'll be a bad mistake for you to go live with him, even for a few days. If he wanted . . ."

"But I'm not falling in love with him!" Katherine protested too vehemently. "Where in the world did you get such a silly idea?"

"I wasn't born yesterday and your eyes are as easy to read as a book." Mallie shook her head indulgently. "I know that man means something to you and you're lying to me and maybe even to yourself if you say he doesn't."

Katherine sighed in surrender. "Okay, okay, maybe he does mean something to me. But I'm not in love with him. And even if I were, I'd never let him know it, so you don't have to worry that he might take advantage of me while I stay with him for a few days. He thinks I'm a child, anyway."

Mallie's intent gaze wandered along Katherine's long, slender, lightly tanned legs over the curve of her hips and upward past the narrow waist to the rounded fullness of her breasts. She smiled wryly. "I never heard this Jason Roarke is addle-brained, but he must be if he thinks you look like a child. Is that it? Is he a mite off in the head?"

"Of course he isn't. He's a very intelligent man." Switching her suitcase to her left hand, Katherine stopped on her way to the door to give Mallie a kiss. "Now, just stop worrying about me. I can take care of myself, but don't tell my father that. It'll do him good to worry about me a little. At least staying with Jason will force him to drop Wendi."

"Don't you go counting on that," Mallie warned. "I reckon you got your muleheadedness honestly. Mr. Brice is as stubborn as you are and then some. So don't you think you're going to win this fight easy."

"Well, I plan to stick it out until I do win because I'm not coming back here until Wendi's gone," Katherine said firmly, hesitating as she laid her hand on the doorknob. "She did go to the casino with him, didn't she? I certainly don't want to run into her on my way out. I don't think I could even be civil to her."

"She's gone," Mallie said, sniffing disrespectfully. "Told me she had to check out of her hotel. Brassy hussy."

"She's a real winner, all right," Katherine agreed, opening the door. "Well, see you in a few days, Mallie."

"Just you watch out for yourself," Mallie called one last warning. "Some gambling men can charm the birds right outa the trees. Don't you let this Jason Roarke sweet-talk you into doing something you might be sorry for."

"I won't, I promise," Katherine said softly, even as she knew he probably could sweet talk her into just about anything without really putting much effort into it. Yet, as she walked down the hall, she pushed that thought far back in her mind. She was doing what she had to do; now wasn't the time to begin doubting the wisdom of her actions.

Luckily, Jason wasn't home when Katherine arrived and his housekeeper was also out. When Katherine walked around to the back door of the A-frame, only Georgia was there, sprawled out under a tree, napping in an almost unconscious stupor as young animals are prone to do. When Katherine whistled for her, she lifted her head lazily and it took a moment or two for her to muster the energy to get up. Suddenly, she came alive, her long, colt-like legs tangling with each other as she propelled herself down a gentle incline toward Katherine.

"At least you're glad to see me," Katherine said to her as she bounded around her feet clumsily. "I just hope your master doesn't react in the opposite way when he comes home tonight." While Georgia plopped down and gnawed blissfully on the corner of the suitcase, Katherine found the key in the potted fern by the back door, where she had seen Jason put it when he had taken her home after bandaging her knee. She had used it before, every evening she had come to stay with him when he had been ill, so it didn't seem so odd now to be walking into his house uninvited. Of course her motives for being here this time were more selfish so she did feel a slight twinge of guilt until it was banished by the sight of Georgia careening across the slippery tile of the kitchen floor, all four feet sliding in different directions.

Katherine took her belongings up to the small bedroom. After unpacking, she eyed the brass bed, wondering how easily sleep would come to her tonight. Not very easily, she suspected, since she wouldn't be able to forget Jason was in the very next room.

By seven o'clock, Katherine decided Jason wasn't coming home for dinner so she made herself a salad and while she ate it, had to endure Georgia's soulful black eyes watching every forkful go into her mouth. After washing the dishes, Katherine gave in and treated the overgrown puppy to a morsel of ham from the plate of fresh cold cuts in the refrigerator. Then Georgia trotted at her heels as she wandered into the great room to stand for a moment, trying to decide what to do to occupy herself until Jason returned. She noticed again the typewriter on a table beside the desk and strolled across the room to take a look, considering writing a letter to her mother on it. But it was a very expensive electric so she decided not to use it. She was dreading Jason's homecoming enough already.

There was always the possibility that he might be displeased to find her here so she didn't want to add to her misery by having to tell him she had jammed up his typewriter, too.

Ultimately, Katherine chose not to write to her mother at all. She would have hated to lie and say everything was fine here at Tahoe, yet she knew she could hardly tell her mother she had moved in with a man, simply to teach her father a lesson. That message, she was certain, would have caused quite an uproar in Baltimore.

Instead, Katherine decided to continue reading the novel she had brought along, the same Gothic romance she had left on the beach that first day she had talked to Jason. In the quiet of the great room, she was soon caught up in the mysterious machinations of all the suspicious characters at a brooding old English estate. The plot became increasingly menacing and it was with reluctance that Katherine took Georgia outside for a few minutes around eleven o'clock. The dog wandered into the shadows, but Katherine stayed within the area illuminated by the brass lamp mounted beside the front door. A distant rumble of thunder sent Georgia scurrying back to the house and Katherine looked up at the thick, dark clouds swirling overhead, obscuring the quarter moon and twinkling stars. A brisk wind swayed the tops of the tall pine trees. When a distant flare of lightning brightened the sky, Georgia cowered close to Katherine's legs as they hurried back inside.

Soon it began to rain softly as Tahoe caught the fringe of the distant storm. Huge drops splattered the windowpanes and pattered noisily on the ground outside. On the Navajo rug, Georgia shifted positions restlessly while Katherine sat on the sofa, her feet tucked up beside her. She continued her reading and unluckily at the same moment the heroine realized she was not alone in the shadowy attic in the English mansion, every light in Jason's house went out. Though they flickered once then flared back on again almost immediately, the damage was done. With a whimper, Georgia leapt up on the sofa to press her furry trembling body as close as possible to Katherine.

A twig snapped sharply outside the front window. Katherine jumped and Georgia gave a low, ominous growl. But her small surge of courage died a quick death. She whimpered again as something moving clumsily outside rustled the evergreen shrubbery. Until that moment, Katherine had hoped they were hearing Jason, but now she knew it couldn't be him. He wouldn't be crashing through the shrubbery in the middle of a rainstorm. So what was outside?

The mystery was soon solved. A cat mewed plaintively and Katherine breathed a hearty sigh of relief. But Georgia whined again and scrunched closer to Katherine's arm. "Oh, it's just a kitty, you silly," Katherine chided gently. "Some protectress you are. You're supposed to bark and growl when you hear strange noises, not hide behind me." As the big black eyes regarded her woefully, she relented, stroking the dog's fluffy fur. "But I guess you're still just a puppy, aren't you?"

Georgia's tail thumped on the sofa cushion in response.

"Okay, now that the bad old cat has gone, you can go back onto the floor," It took some urging, but Katherine managed to persuade Georgia to make her bed on the Navajo rug again and exhausted by the scary events, she sprawled out immediately and went to sleep.

Katherine stretched out on the sofa to read awhile longer, but after only a few minutes she began to yawn. She shut the book on her finger to keep her place, then closed her eyes, intending only to rest them for a few seconds.

Light, gentle fingers threading through her hair awakened her some time later. She stirred lazily, then her eyes flickered open. "Jason," she whispered, gazing up at him, fascinated by the way his sun-streaked hair glinted in the soft lamplight. When she struggled to sit up, his hands curved around her waist and she found herself very close to him.

"Kit, why are you here?" he asked quietly, smoothing her tousled hair back from her face. "Is something wrong?"

"No. Well, yes, sort of," she answered nervously, then proceeded to nibble a fingernail. He was too close. She could feel the warmth emanating from his body and the disturbing lime fragrance of his aftershave aroused memories of those occasions when she had been even closer to him. Scooting back slightly away from him, she smiled shyly, then the words began tumbling from her as she explained about her father and Wendi. When she had finished, and Jason only gazed at her silently, she bent her head, murmuring, "Well, I guess you can't understand why I'm upset. His involvement with Wendi must seem perfectly all right to you."

A resigned smile curved Jason's lips as he shook his head. "You're still assuming I'm just like your father, aren't you, Kit?" he asked, raking long fingers through his hair as his other hand tightened around her waist. "You shouldn't make assumptions like that. They're not always correct and this is one of those times. I *do* understand why you're upset, but I also think you have to begin to accept the fact that your father doesn't live his life exactly the way you want him to."

"Fine," Katherine responded crisply. "But he'll have to accept the fact that I won't stay in the same house with him as long as he insists on making a fool of himself with Wendi Miller."

Lifting her chin in one large hand, Jason held her gaze. "And is that why you're here?"

She nodded. "Let me stay, please," she blurted out, her tone beseeching. "I'll try not to get in your way. I just want him to understand how I felt when Wendi came sauntering in this morning, acting as if she owned the place. It was so very obvious that they're much more than casual friends."

Jason lifted one dark eyebrow quizzically. "You're something of a paradox, Kit. You assume I'm just like your father, that I'm interested in women only as sex objects, yet you obviously trust me enough to stay here with me. Aren't you afraid I'll try to take advantage of you?"

Unsurprisingly, she blushed. "I . . . I think I can trust you. Can't I?" she asked hopefully. Then she gave a little shrug and bent her head to conceal her eyes from his keen observation. "Besides, you've implied I'm so inexperienced that you wouldn't be interested in . . . in . . ."

"Oh, I'm interested, all right," he murmured, his voice deep and disturbingly husky. He drew her closer, his lean hands on her bare midriff gently squeezing and caressing. His lips grazed her smooth jaw over to her small chin, then slowly upward toward her mouth. "I told you once that your innocence is enchanting." His mouth barely touched hers, and as her lips parted with a swift intake of breath and she trembled, he lifted his head, the darkening blue of his eyes enveloping her in a warm light that hinted at barely restrained desire. "You see what I mean? You say you think you can trust me yet when I touch you, you tremble." He pressed his hand against her, the heel of his palm resting on the firm cushioned swell of her breasts, his fingertips brushing her collarbone. "And your heart is pounding, Kit. Are you that afraid of me?"

"Yes. No. Oh, sometimes I am," she answered breathlessly, chewing her lower lip. Her wide green eyes were dark with confusion as she gazed up at him. "You're a paradox, too," she whispered. "I never know what you might do. Like . . . like right now, I . . . I don't know what you're thinking. I don't know if you . . . want me."

"I always want you, Kit," he admitted unashamedly, a slight indulgent smile lifting the corners of his mouth. "You're a very desirable young woman and I want to make love to you. But not if you allow it to happen just to get back at your father. When I make love to you, it'll be because you want me to, because you're responding to me the way you did that day in my bedroom. Remember?"

Nodding, nearly mesmerized by the memory his words evoked, she swayed toward him, then felt unreasonably disappointed when he suddenly released her and stood, thrusting his hands into his cream-colored trouser pockets.

His expression became unreadable. "But you don't have to worry about that tonight. It's nearly two and you look very tired. I suggest we go to bed. In separate rooms, of course."

Though his tone was unmistakably teasing, Katherine blushed again, but obvious relief relaxed her delicate features. "Then you *are* going to let me stay?"

"If you want to know the truth, Kit, I think you should go home," he answered candidly. "Problems are rarely solved by running away from them."

Katherine pressed her lips together stubbornly. "I won't go back to that house until my father stops seeing Wendi. So if you don't want me here, would you drive me to a hotel?"

"No. You can stay here, Kit," he responded, regarding her intently, a muscle ticking in his tightened jaw. "But you'd better remember what I said. If you respond to me the way you did that day in my bedroom, then I . . ."

He never finished the warning. He didn't have to. To Katherine, the message was tantalizingly clear.

"Kit, wake up," Jason was saying, brushing Katherine's thick braid back over her shoulder. When her eyes flickered open, then dilated and widened with confusion and some fear, he smiled gently. "You have to get up, Kit. Your father's here and he's demanding to see you."

Katherine was wide awake immediately. She sat up straight in the bed and as Jason's lazy gaze drifted down to the low neckline of her white cotton gown, she clutched the sheet up close under her chin. "Wh-What do you mean he's demanding to see me? Is he that furious?"

"He certainly isn't pleased that you stayed here all night," Jason answered with a wry smile as he rose from the edge of the bed where he had been sitting. "And he isn't pleased with me. He looked at me as if he thinks I instigated this entire situation."

Katherine grimaced apologetically. "I'm sorry; I know you probably don't want to get involved with all this, but . . ."

"But you want him to believe we're lovers," Jason finished for her, then lifted his broad shoulders in a shrug. "Well, judging by the expression on his face when I answered the door, he's very worried that we might be. So your little ploy could work, I suppose. Then again, it might backfire. Brice doesn't impress me as the kind of man who would appreciate being manipulated. He may not let you force him to end his relationship with Wendi. If he's as stubborn as you are, I don't imagine he will."

"That's what Mallie said—she's our housekeeper. She knows my father pretty well," Katherine said musingly, then sighed as she met Jason's dark gaze. "But I have to try, don't I? And you'll play along with me, won't you? I mean, you don't have to act like you're my lover or anything like that. Just try to pretend you don't mind having me here. Please."

"I think I'm already involved in this little plot," Jason said with a rueful smile. "I thought for a moment Brice was going to throw a punch at me when I answered the door in this bathrobe."

Swallowing with some difficulty, Katherine allowed herself to look at him closely for the first time since he had awakened her. Clad only in a short terry cloth robe, he certainly looked the part of the virile lover. Her bemused gaze lingered on the brown, hair-roughened expanse of chest exposed where the robe's lapels came together and she needed no more than a quick glance at his long, muscular legs to set her heart pounding. Her eyes darted upward again to the sleep-tousled thickness of his golden hair and then, almost against her will, she was staring at the sensuous curve of his chiseled mouth.

"Get dressed, Kit," he commanded brusquely, turning to go to the door. "If you don't come down soon, I have the feeling Brice will come up here after you."

When Jason had gone, Katherine drew a deep, shuddering breath. The feelings he aroused in her might make it very easy for her to act as if her father had reason to worry about her staying here. Throwing back the covers, she got out of bed, catching sight of her reflection in the full-length mirror on the opposite wall. Yes, her feelings for Jason did seem to be mirrored in dreamy soft eyes and the sensuous curve of her slightly parted lips. But this nightgown would never do, she decided, eyeing herself critically. The white cotton fabric was not sheer enough and the gown even had tiny rosebuds embroidered around the scooped neckline. It was much too demure. And with her hair confined in a fat braid, she looked too young and innocent. Somehow, she wanted to go downstairs looking as if she might have just spent a night wild with passion and after a moment's deliberation, she knew exactly what to do.

She tiptoed out of her room, down the short hall to Jason's. His bed was unmade but she saw no discarded pajamas anywhere. She decided Jason probably slept nude, then refused to allow her imagination to elaborate on that thought as she went to his closet and boldly removed a short silk-like navy robe from a hanger. After pulling her gown off over her head, she put on the robe, rolled up the cuffs around her wrists, then tied the belt loosely at her waist. Stepping in front of the mirror, she was pleased to see that the too-large robe made her look quite suitably *en déshabillé*. Feeling her attire was provocative enough to shock her father, she then started on her hair, undoing the braid so that the gold-highlighted auburn strands swung free around her waist. She ran her fingers through the silky thickness, tousling it around her face. After assuming what she hoped seemed a sensuous expression, she was ready.

Walking down the steps to the great room was the most difficult task she had ever undertaken. But it had to be done, she told herself repeatedly, and the stubborn streak in her urged her onward. Barefoot, she descended noiselessly. As she reached the foot of the stairs, neither Jason nor her father had noticed her yet so she had time to take a deep breath to fortify her courage.

"Morning," she drawled as she strolled lazily across the room. Ignoring her father's sharply indrawn breath, she stopped by the chair where Jason sat, gave him a sleepy little smile, then casually dropped her hand down to rest on his shoulder as she finally met her father's eyes. He was glowering at her as if he could gladly turn her over his knee. Every muscle in his body seemed tensed and it took all the self-control she could muster not to run and hide somewhere. But she stood her ground, saying nothing, simply looking at him.

"What the devil do you mean coming down here dressed like that?" Brice growled, his hands balled into tight fists on the arms of his chair. "And what are you doing here in the first place? What are you trying to prove?"

"Why, nothing," Katherine answered, assuming her most innocent expression. "I just felt like moving in with

Jason for a while. I didn't really want to stay there with you as long as you're running around with Wendi Miller. Didn't Mallie tell you that?"

Brice leaned forward, his expression menacingly grim. "Mallie tried to reach me all last evening, but unfortunately I wasn't at the casino. When I got home about three this morning, she'd finally gone to sleep. But she certainly told me you were here and why as soon as she woke up this morning. She's worried about you. And I'm mad as hell. So go pack your things, Katherine. I'm taking you home right now."

"I don't think so," Katherine answered as calmly as she could, glancing down at Jason as he looked up at her. There was a definite hint of amusement dancing in his eyes and for some odd reason, that renewed her courage. She looked back at her father, tilting her chin up in defiance. "I will not go home as long as you keep seeing Wendi and that's final."

Brice exploded. "You'll do as I tell you! And you won't coerce me into doing what you want me to! I'll see Wendi if I want to. I don't intend to let you run my life. You're the child, not the parent, and if you don't start remembering that, I may be tempted to give you the first spanking you've ever had from me."

His vehemence merely reinforced her obstinance. She glared at him, trying to look fierce, unaware of the fact that she presented just the opposite picture. There was a lot of Jason's robe but very little of her and her slenderness was accentuated. Even the determined expression on her face could not disguise her delicate, nearly childlike features. She looked vulnerable and apparently Brice recognized that because he turned his attention to Jason.

"We're not close friends, Roarke," he began grimly, his green eyes hard. "But I thought I knew you well enough to logically assume you wouldn't take advantage of a child as inexperienced as Kit. I guess I was wrong."

Jason tensed. "I can assure you Kit is as innocent this morning as she was when she arrived here last night," he said flatly. Then ignoring Brice's audible sigh of relief and the impatient glance Katherine shot him, he qualified his statement. "But, Brice, Kit is no child. She's twenty-one and I have to be honest and tell you that I'm attracted to her. And I have every indication to believe she's attracted to me, too. So, although nothing happened between us last night, I can't promise you nothing ever will, especially if she lives in this house with me."

A thunderous expression appeared on Brice's face, then he turned to Katherine. "I'm disappointed in you, Kit," he muttered, his voice harsh. "You're playing with fire. Jason is far too old for you and you'll end up hurt if you're not very careful. I can't believe you'd risk that just to force me to do what you want. So go upstairs like a good girl and pack and I'll take you home where you belong."

"If Jason's too old for me, then you're much much too old for Wendi," Katherine replied as casually as possible. "So as long as you insist on seeing her, I plan to stay right here with Jason."

Uttering an explicit curse, Brice jumped to his feet. "No daughter of mine is going to tell me how to live my life. So I'll leave without you. When you come to your senses, let me know. I'll come take you home."

After casting a threatening glare in Jason's direction, he stormed out of the house, slamming the front door shut behind him.

Katherine's shoulders drooped then she glanced warily at Jason as he got up to stand before her. "It looks like you're stuck with me for a while, until he changes his mind." She gave a weak, apologetic smile. "I'll try not to bother you much, really I will. And thank you for saying what you did about being . . . attracted to me. You made the situation sound very convincing."

"I was just being honest, Kit, so don't make the mistake

of thinking you're perfectly safe with me," he murmured softly, hot light flaring in his dark blue eyes as they roamed freely over her. "Remember what I told you last night—I want to make love to you. So, if you have any desire to hold onto your virginity, you'd be wise to wear something less enticing than you have on right now. I'm a man, not a saint and I can only resist temptation so long. So be careful. Understand?"

As he reached out without warning to cup her firm warm breasts in his hard yet gentle hands, she gasped softly. His eyes narrowed. He moved closer. For a second she tensed, unable to move. Then with a muffled little cry of pure fright, she turned and fled, flying up the stairs to her room. Her breath came in short soft gasps as she closed the door and leaned against it. Oh, she understood all right. Perfectly.

Chapter Eight

On Wednesday morning, a week later, Katherine stepped out of her bedroom into the hall, stifling a yawn behind her hand. Even during holidays, she usually woke up by eight o'clock each morning but she was a slow starter. It took some time to really awaken completely and today was no exception. Pausing for a moment by her door, she arched her body with the lissome fluidity of youth, crossing her arms behind her head as she stretched lazily. Suddenly, a strange sensation trickling along her spine warned her that she was not alone in the hall. She spun around hastily on one heel, found Jason standing by his own door, and as she swiftly lowered her arms, she tugged at the bottom of her pale green T-shirt, inadvertently emphasizing the firm round fullness of her breasts. But as Jason's dark gaze drifted downward and his jaw tightened slightly, she nervously released her shirttail and slipped her hands into the pockets of her denim cut-offs. "Good

121

morning," she murmured, her voice still enticingly husky with sleepiness. As he merely inclined his head, still gazing intently at her, she gave him a half-shy smile. Clad in khaki-colored chinos and a navy knit shirt, he seemed to exude an aura of virile masculinity and without conscious thought, she took a step toward him, then stopped, raising one hand in a gesture of uncertainty. "Would you . . . I mean, since Mary isn't coming in today, would you like me to make you some breakfast?"

He shook his head. "No, thank you. I've been up for over an hour and I've already made breakfast for myself."

"Really?" Her delicately arched brown eyebrows lifted. "I didn't realize you could cook."

"Why are you so surprised?" he asked rather irritably. "Did you imagine I could do little else besides shuffle cards?"

"Oh, no, that's not what I meant at all!" Anxious to convince him, she took several steps toward him, spreading her hands in an apologetic gesture. "Since most men aren't particularly proficient in the kitchen, I . . . I just thought you wouldn't be, either. Heaven knows, my father can't even boil water so . . ."

"There you go again, Kit—assuming I'm a carbon copy of Brice." With one long stride, Jason eliminated the distance between them. His hard hands closed around her shapely upper arms, his unusually rough grip indicating to some degree the depth of his impatience. "What do I have to do to convince you that all men aren't exactly alike, not even professional gamblers? Why is it so difficult for you to understand that I'm really not much like your father? I'm an individual, a totally different man."

She gazed up at his lean, tanned face, bemused by his serious tone and by the seemingly searching light in his narrowed eyes. The tip of her tongue came out to moisten her suddenly dry lips. Shaking her head, she averted her eyes, unable to withstand his piercing gaze any longer.

"I . . . I do know you're different or at least you seem to be." She bent her head, her silken auburn hair falling forward like a curtain against her cheeks. Chewing her upper lip, she tried to find the precise words to make him understand how ambiguous her feelings were. With a soft sigh, she began haltingly, "In my head, I do know you're different, but . . . but all my life, deep down inside, I've . . . I've . . ."

"Believed all gamblers are shallow, selfish, and completely untrustworthy," Jason finished for her, not with a question but with a statement of fact. His hard hands released her arms and his touch became gentle as he cupped her slender neck, tilting her chin up with both his thumbs. "How tender do I have to be with you, Kit, before you realize I'm not that way?" Without waiting for an answer, he lowered his head.

As his mouth covered hers, warm, firm, and caressingly gentle, Katherine swayed closer to him, a sweet poignant weakness draining all the strength from her limbs. One muscular arm encircled her slender waist and the soft curves of her young body merged with the lean, muscular contours of his, as if they had been proportioned perfectly for each other. His teeth closed lightly on the full curve of her lower lip, tugging her mouth open beneath his. Brushing fingers moved around her neck, slipping through the long strands of silken hair past her waist. Both his hands covered the rounded firmness of her hips, exerting a light pressure that brought her against his hard thighs and his upsurging response to her nearness sent her senses reeling.

"You know what you do to me, Kit," he murmured huskily, his warm breath caressing her ear. "I need you and it's not easy to be gentle, but I'm trying. Doesn't that count for something?"

In answer, she moved closer, losing herself in the sweet tumult of delight aroused by his words and by caresses that conveyed a promise of searing passion. Yet, as he freed her shirt from the waistband of her shorts and his hands sought her firm full breasts, she trembled as his fingertips possessively stroked the throbbing aroused peaks, scorching her skin even through the lace of her bra. She wanted him to go on touching her forever and as she realized how easy it would be to surrender completely, she uttered a soft protest, tensing as she moved slightly away from him.

With a muttered imprecation, he dropped his hands to her waist again and brushed his lips across the tousled hair atop her head. "Kit, what am I going to do with you?" he whispered roughly, raising his head, tilting her chin up with one long, lean finger so that she had to look at him. "I want you so much but even when I'm very gentle with you, you're still afraid of me. Why? Because you begin to want me, too? Are you really that afraid of becoming involved with me?"

With his piercing blue eyes impaling hers, she couldn't lie to him. Finally, reluctantly, she nodded. "But, Jason, I . . ."

"You don't remind me as much of my ex-wife as I thought, Kit," he interrupted musingly. "Denise was never afraid of our relationship. She simply hated my . . . profession because it didn't provide enough security to suit her, financial security, that is. But then, she wasn't the romantic little virgin you are, even when I first met her. It isn't financial security you're seeking, is it? You want emotional security?"

Swallowing with difficulty, she nodded again. "Yes, I guess, and . . ."

"And you're certain you'd never feel secure with me because I'm a gambler—like your father," Jason finished for her, shaking his head. His hands dropped from around her waist as he took a backward step, surveying her, the expression on his sun-browned face enigmatic.

As he raked long fingers through his thick sun-bleached

hair, his simple Nordic good looks were enough of a temptation for Katherine and with the unbidden memory of his deep melodious voice saying her name, she ached to fling herself back into his arms and urge him to make love to her. Conflicting emotions tore at her, but at last the self-protecting wall she had erected around herself because of her father's desertion proved too strong. Even her growing respect and need for Jason couldn't crumble her defenses and she lowered her head, veiling the confusion and unhappiness in her eyes with the thick fringe of her lashes.

"I have to go out, Kit," Jason said gruffly, stepping around her as he walked to the head of the stairs. "I may be gone most of the day. Do you have something to keep you occupied?"

Gnawing her lower lip, she nodded. "Jess asked me to join her for lunch."

Striding briskly down the steps as if eager to escape her, Jason muttered back over his shoulder, "See you later, then."

"Later," she answered almost inaudibly, an oppressive heaviness settling in her chest as she watched him go out the front door and close it behind him. With a heartfelt sigh, she trudged down the stairs and walked into the kitchen. She opened the refrigerator and surveyed the contents, then closed it again, knowing that mere food couldn't ease the emptiness she felt inside.

As Katherine adjusted one narrow strap of the saffron sundress she wore, she peered into the dimly lighted Italian restaurant, at last spying Jess sitting at a small table in the far right corner. Ignoring the admiring glances of a few companionless men, she threaded her way between the intimate tables for two, subsiding with a sigh in the chair across from Jess.

Dressed in a powder blue suit that complimented her

strawberry blond hair, Jess smiled questioningly at her. "Was that a tired sigh or a sad sigh, Kit?"

"Neither. Or maybe both," Katherine answered evasively, unnecessarily smoothing her hair back toward the loose chignon on her nape. "Or maybe it's just the heat. Mallie had some shopping to do so she drove me here in the jeep. And the sun's very hot today. I feel sort of washed out."

"I certainly know that feeling," Jess said, lifting her hand to beckon a mustachioed waiter. After both she and Kit had made a selection from the menu and the waiter had gone away again, she gave the younger girl a wan smile. "Well, tell me, are you enjoying the summer?"

Katherine shrugged noncommittally, unwilling to confess that Jason Roarke was making this the most exciting summer she had ever spent, as well as the most unnerving. Somehow, Jess didn't appear to be in a receptive mood to share confidences today so Katherine chose to keep her secrets to herself, though it would have been comforting to blurt out all her conflicting emotions in the hope that Jess could help her make some sense of them. But, since the older woman seemed preoccupied, Katherine only nodded briefly. "I'm enjoying this summer as much as any, I guess."

"That's good," Jess murmured absently, then said nothing more even after the waiter served the antipasto.

Katherine eyed the secretary speculatively as they both partook of what was actually the aperitif, rolls of narrow slices of delicately cured ham, which was tender and quite delicious served with iced fresh melon balls. Yet, Jess ate automatically, without any apparent enjoyment and since Katherine's appetite had not really returned after her confrontation with Jason that morning, she too had lost all desire for food by the time the main course was served.

Something was wrong with Jess. Though she was naturally fair-skinned, her cheeks were almost pallid today and there were tiny, barely discernible lines of strain around her mouth. Most noticeable, however, was the loss of sparkle in her dark brown eyes. Now there was an almost haunted luminosity in them that worried Katherine considerably. Finally, after staring down at her plateful of cappelletti—varied-shaped pastas filled with meat and seasoned with tomato and mushroom sauce—Katherine sighed again, laying her fork aside.

"I'll tell you why I feel rotten if you'll tell me why you do," she suggested with a rueful little smile. "Deal?"

In response, Jess forced a wan smile that only succeeded in making her look sadder still. "I don't really feel rotten . . . Well, yes, I guess I do." Lifting her head to look at Katherine, her brown eyes abruptly glistened with tears. "I'm thinking of . . . leaving Tahoe," she mumbled thickly. "I–I'm beginning to see that I should give up on . . . on Brice. It's time to stop wishing for something that can never happen; it's time for me to leave him, Kit."

Katherine had never been so shocked in her life. Though she herself had advised Jess to leave her father, she had never really expected the older woman to take that advice. She was too loyal and obviously too much in love to recognize Brice Delacorte's shortcomings—at least, she had been too loyal until now. But apparently something had happened recently to change her mind and Katherine was nearly afraid to ask what her father had done to hurt Jess badly enough that she had decided to leave him. Yet, she had to know.

"Why, Jess?" she asked softly, her own green eyes filling with commiserative tears as the older woman hastily dried hers with a tissue. "When I first got here this summer and talked to you about my father, you made it sound as if you'd never leave him. What's he done to make you change your mind?"

Stiffening her spine in an obvious effort to regain control of her emotions, Jess smiled humorlessly. "Believe it or not, it's that little idiot, Wendi, who's changed my mind. I thought she would be just like all the other women he's been involved with over the years—here today, gone tomorrow. But she's different. He's getting more involved with her than he did with any of the others. I mean, after all, he's practically given her the run of his house, even though you're there."

"Oh, but I'm *not* there," Katherine protested vehemently, her jaw tightening. "I thought you knew—as soon as I realized he was involved with her, I moved out. I wasn't about to live in the same house with him while he runs around with that 'brassy hussy,' as Mallie calls her."

"But Brice never mentioned that you'd moved out!" Jess said, shaking her head incredulously. "I had no idea. I thought you were still there with him. Where *are* you staying then? Which hotel?"

"I'm not staying at a hotel," Katherine answered reluctantly, then proceeded to explain her situation. After finishing, she breathed an inward sigh as she saw the disapproving frown mar Jess's forehead. She expected a sermon and she got one.

"Kit, that's the craziest idea I've ever heard," Jess declared firmly, making no attempt to be diplomatic. "Even if you had a chance of making Brice change his mind about Wendi, which you don't, you'd still be taking a terrific risk by living with Jason Roarke. I wasn't even aware you had met the man, much less knew him well enough to go live with him!"

"I know Jason pretty well, I guess," Katherine murmured, ignoring the heat that suffused her cheeks. "Besides, I just sort of barged in on him when I left home because of Wendi. He didn't have much choice but to let me stay there. The next day he didn't ask me to leave so I stayed. He seems to understand I just want to teach my father a lesson."

"And he expects nothing from you in return for a place

to stay?" Jess interrogated sharply, obviously finding that possibility hard to believe. "Oh Kit, I do hope you haven't done something you'll regret for the rest of your life."

"I haven't, so don't worry," Katherine assured her, dismissing that subject with a wave of her hand. "Now, let's talk about you again. Why are you so upset about Wendi? Just because my father's seeing her doesn't mean . . ."

"It's not only that," Jess interrupted wearily, massaging the back of her neck with one hand. "She's more important to him than the others were, apparently even more important than I realized if he goes on seeing her, although you moved in with Jason Roarke because he was. I'm astounded that Brice doesn't just drop her so you'll come home again. It doesn't make any sense."

"Maybe he's just being stubborn," Katherine suggested weakly, in an attempt at consolation. "Mallie says he can be as bull-headed as I am and, heaven knows, I'm being very obstinate as far as Wendi's concerned."

Jess shook her head, lowering her eyes to the checked tablecloth again. "No, Kit, Brice isn't *that* stubborn. He'd never let you live with a man like Jason Roarke, a man no one knows anything about, simply to avoid conceding defeat. So Wendi must mean a great deal to him, though I don't know why. She's such an obvious gold digger and a giggling, simpleminded woman—quite obnoxious, frankly. But Brice doesn't seem to realize that."

"But he will, I'm certain of it. Just give him some time and I'll bet he throws her out on her ear."

"Don't count on that, Kit," Jess heaved a sigh. "I know Brice and he's always loathed possessive women but, though Wendi tries to spend every minute with him, I've never seen him get impatient with her. Whenever she asks for money, which is often, he always gives it to her."

"Surely he's bright enough to realize she's just using him!" Katherine exclaimed softly. "Good heavens, as soon as he manages to persuade one of the hotels to take her on as a singer, she'll drop him like a hot potato. And he knows that."

"I'm not so sure he's even trying to persuade anyone to hire her anymore. I heard she was a pretty lousy singer," Jess explained ruefully. "And what's worse is that she's beginning to realize she is so I think she's decided if she can't have a glamorous career, she'll grab the next best thing—a husband with some money who lives a fairly glamorous life."

Katherine's eyes widened. "You mean . . ."

"I mean, she'd marry Brice so fast it would make your head swim, if he asked her. He's a wealthy man, Kit. He was a very successful gambler and he invested his winnings and now, of course, he gets a percentage of the take at the casino."

"But he'd never ask her!" Katherine cried softly, then added hopefully, "Would he? How could he? She's nothing but an opportunist! What can he see in her? She's so silly and shallow."

"Oh, Kit, you're such an innocent," Jess commented, though not unkindly. "You really don't think she acts that way around him, do you? Heavens, no! All he sees is the petite little woman who's tried so hard to make her way in a cold, cruel world for the past five or six years. She may arouse his protective instincts and, of course, she is pretty. Any man would be attracted to her. So maybe Brice is finally falling in love. He never has since his marriage to your mother ended, but I thought if I just stuck by him that maybe some day, he'd fall in love with me. But it didn't work out that way, did it?"

"He couldn't choose her over you," Katherine whispered urgently, trying to convince herself as much as Jess. "I haven't always liked my father and the way he lives, but I know he isn't stupid. And you must know that, too. Or you never would have fallen in love with him."

"Oh, Kit, I'm not sure I know anything anymore," Jess said wearily. "I thought I knew Brice better than anybody ever had, except maybe your mother. He's always been such a reserved person; you know that, but he wasn't that way with me so I assumed that meant I was something special to him. When I first met him ten years ago, he really swept me off my feet. I was twenty-eight, but I'd never been really involved with a man before and Brice was so witty and sophisticated. Besides, nobody else seemed able to get close to him. But with me, he was warm and caring and he seemed to need me so much."

Katherine felt the blood drain from her cheeks and the tensing of her stomach muscles nearly made her feel ill. It was as if she had just heard her own relationship with Jason described in perfect detail. No one knew much about him either, yet, with her, he was a warm, caring man, even in their more passionate moments together. He seemed so open with his feelings, unhesitatingly confessing his need for her and because of that very forthright openness, he had caused her to trust him far more than she had ever intended.

It was ironic. She had always assumed Jason was like her father in many ways—irresponsible, pleasure seeking, and incapable of making lasting personal commitments. But she had also assumed that the two men had totally different personalities. Jason was such a charming rogue yet surprisingly perceptive and even serious on occasion while her father seemed such a brooding, unapproachable man. Yet, Jess said with her, he had been witty and warm, so charmingly irresistible that she had fallen in love with him. Katherine was astounded by this knowledge and greatly dismayed. Now it appeared she should have been trusting Jason less rather than more with each passing day because he was far more like her father than she had ever imagined.

Jess's revelation seemed like an ominous warning to

Katherine of what her future might be if she allowed herself to become too involved with Jason. Staring fixedly at the older woman, she murmured, "You know, Jason seems very warm and caring when he's with me. I thought that, at least, made him different from my father."

"*Kit,*" Jess whispered, her mouth twisting sympathetically. "You're really attracted to him, aren't you? Oh, do be careful. Please, be very careful."

Katherine stared down at the bright red and white checked tablecloth. "Odd, isn't it? I swore I'd never get involved with any man even remotely like my father. For a while I did try not to be drawn to Jason. But he did seem different. Father's never been terribly warm toward me but, Jason . . ." She hesitated, pressing her fingertips against the throbbing ache that was beginning to build in her temples. Shaking her head, she attempted a smile that didn't quite reach her eyes. "My, my, we're a couple of susceptible babes when it comes to wolves in sheep's clothing, aren't we, Jess?"

"Honey," Jess murmured, reaching across the table to briefly touch her arm, "I really don't know what to say to you."

"You could tell me I'd better get away from Jason Roarke as fast as I can," Katherine answered grimly, twisting her linen napkin around her fingers. "That's what you want to tell me, isn't it? You're thinking of leaving my father, aren't you? Don't you want to tell me not to waste ten years of my life on a man like him, the way you feel you wasted yours?"

Tugging a strand of her hair, Jess shrugged. "Maybe I should have had the sense to leave Brice nine years ago. I might have found a man I could at least be content with; I might even have had children. But I didn't go and since I'm a bit too old to think of having children now, maybe I should just stay here." Her brown eyes darkened with confusion even as she chuckled mirthlessly. "Too bad

Brad's vacation ended and he went back to Philadelphia. If he were still here, I'd know exactly what to do. I'd stay just to spite him. He's my brother, but he can be such a pious bore, especially when he's pestering me to leave Tahoe."

Katherine couldn't muster even a slight answering smile. Faced with the realization that her feelings for Jason had gone beyond her control, she desperately needed advice. "Jason's become too important to me. I never meant to let him but he has," she confessed miserably. "Please, tell me what to do."

"Oh, Kit, what do I know?" Jess exclaimed softly. "I'm such a fool about your father that most of the time, I don't regret a moment of those months we had together ten years ago. I . . ." She halted abruptly, her expression hardening as she stared past Katherine toward the restaurant entrance. Inclining her head slightly in that direction, she added tautly, "Then there are times like this, when I wish I'd never seen Brice Delacorte's face."

Detecting the pain in her brown eyes, Katherine glanced over her shoulder, her lips pressing together as she saw her father and Wendi approaching the table. Turning back to Jess, she rose to her feet. "Let's get out of here, okay?"

"Please." Rising also, Jess lifted her chin proudly, murmuring, "She hates me, you know. She deliberately drags Brice where she knows I'll be so I'll have to see them together. She knows I love him and would like nothing more than for me to quit my job and leave Tahoe."

"Then if I were you, I'd die before I left," Katherine whispered, eliciting a smile from Jess and returning it as Brice and Wendi reached them.

"Jess, Kit," Brice murmured, a half smile twitching at the corners of his mouth. "Care to join us for a drink before you go?"

"I'm late. Sorry," Jess said flatly, squeezing Katherine's

arm in farewell before she sidestepped the couple and strolled away with great dignity.

"How about you, Kit?" Brice asked. "You and I have something to discuss and I'd like to arrange a time to talk to you. So why don't you join us now."

"Oh, please do," Wendi crooned, hanging onto Brice's arm as if she might fall down flat without him to support her. The smile she gave Katherine was too sugary to be genuine. "Stay and talk to us awhile. I never see you and that's silly. Don't you think? I feel like part of the family now so we should be good friends, me and you."

Fat chance, Katherine almost retorted but instead she managed a fairly credible smile. "I don't have time for a drink, either," she answered, hardly aware of her resentful expression as she glanced up at her father. "If I want a ride home, I have to meet Mallie in about two minutes. So, see you later." Without waiting for a reply, she too made a dignified, unhurried exit from the restaurant. Yet as she stepped out onto the sidewalk, into the fresh clean mountain air, her shoulders abruptly drooped.

Luckily, the outrageous prices at the supermarket had put Mallie in a foul mood. Much to Katherine's relief she talked very little during the short drive from the village to Jason's house. After getting out of the jeep there, Katherine leaned down to smile at the housekeeper through the open window.

"Maybe I'll walk over and see you tomorrow," she suggested softly. "We haven't talked for a while and I've missed you."

"Wouldn't miss me if you was where you oughta be," Mallie grumped, clicking her tongue disapprovingly as she glared at Jason's A-frame house. "You and your daddy are two stubborn mules. You know that? Him running 'round with a hussy and you living with a no 'count gambler and neither one of you married. Beats all I've ever seen in my life. What's this old world coming to?"

Still muttering to herself, she shifted into reverse, giving Katherine one last forceful glare. "You watch out how you act round this man, you hear me. Or you might just land yourself into trouble you never did bargain for. Now, step back from the car so I can get this ice cream home 'fore it melts all over me."

As Mallie turned the jeep around and drove away, Katherine waved, but the smile the housekeeper had elicited faded as she approached Jason's front door. His Jaguar was here so she knew he had returned and she dreaded seeing him. His smile alone could drive all logical thought from her mind until all she could do was wish he would take her in his arms and kiss her.

She was acting like a silly thirteen-year-old, she decided, taking the key Jason had given her from her straw purse and unlocking the door. She stepped into the cool, dim foyer, telling herself she could resist even his considerably potent charm if she really tried. Then as she dropped the door key back into her purse, her ears were assaulted by the shrill sound of a woman's laughter coming from the great room. As Katherine recognized Jason's low melodious tones in response to the laugh, she moved out of the foyer to stand where she could see into the room. An intense jealousy tore through her as she watched Julie, the willowy blonde, drop down on the sofa beside Jason, draping one long bare arm across his shoulders. Feeling rather like a child spying on her elders, Katherine started to turn to walk away but Julie caught sight of her.

"There's your little houseguest, Jason," she declared airily. "I do believe she thinks she's interrupting something and is trying to steal away so she won't disturb us. Come on back, kid. Jason said you might be back soon so you weren't interrupting anyway. Now, five minutes from now might have been a different story."

The woman's suggestive and condescending tone grated on Katherine's nerves. Unable to smile, she simply looked at the couple on the sofa but her pensive gaze lingered mostly on Jason. He steadily maintained the disturbing eye contact. He wasn't smiling, either. His dark blue eyes roamed over her freely as if he were remembering the kisses and caresses they had exchanged that morning. Or was that just wishful thinking on her part? Katherine wondered dismally as Julie suddenly stroked his cheek and he turned to smile at her. Feeling distinctly like a fifth wheel, Katherine muttered something about going up to her room to change her clothes. As she trudged up the stairs, her heart seemed to sink all the way down to her stomach when she heard Jason agree to Julie's suggestion that they go for a long, private drive.

Jason hadn't come home when Katherine went to bed at one the next morning and though she lay awake for hours, hoping to hear him return, he still didn't come. At last, exhausted, she drifted off to sleep, but a sense of foreboding engulfed her as she arose the next morning and dressed. When she stepped out of her room, then started down the stairs, the front door opened and Jason entered the foyer, still dressed in the clothes he had worn yesterday when he had left with Julie. Katherine had suspected he would spend the night with the dancer, but to have that suspicion confirmed was like having a knife twisted in her chest. With all the effort she could muster, she tried to arrange her face into a stony expressionless mask. Suddenly she felt as if she had joined Jess Whitney in that sisterhood of foolish women who fell in love with the wrong men, because, despite all Katherine's firm resolutions, she was in love with Jason. She knew she must be or the thought of him with another woman wouldn't cause her such excruciating pain.

Chapter Nine

It was a gray morning. The sky above Tahoe had been overcast for the past two days. A drizzling rain was falling when Katherine got up on Saturday but it wasn't the sort of cleansing refreshing rain that cools the air. Actually an oppressive mugginess had settled over the lake and along its shore. After brushing her teeth and washing her face, Katherine sought the coolest clothes she owned—a worn pair of denim cut-offs and an equally worn and faded denim halter. She shunned even her sandals, feeling considerably cooler when she could walk around barefoot on the hardwood floors. She re-braided her hair, wound it into a bun on her nape, then left her room.

Poised at the head of the stairs a moment later, she gazed down thoughtfully at Jason's back as he sat at the table in the great room typing steadily again, as he had done almost all of yesterday. What in the world was he doing? she wondered, a slight frown knitting her smooth brow. His preoccupation with that typewriter had begun to pique her curiosity as early as yesterday afternoon. Now that she realized he was beginning another day the same way, she felt an intense desire to discover exactly what he was up to. She was not eager to simply ask him outright. Since her talk with Jess, and especially since he had apparently spent Wednesday night with Julie, Katherine had been trying her best to avoid him. Obviously he had sensed her reluctance to remain in the same room alone with him because he too had become very aloof and sometimes Katherine felt there was a nearly tangible tension between them. It was an uncomfortable situation, at least for her. She could no longer deny to herself that she loved him, yet had to try to protect herself by always hiding what she felt. Consequently, she felt as if she were being pulled in two different directions, which was very wearing on her nerves. Even now, early in the morning, every muscle in her body was tensed as if she were balancing herself on the edge of a precipice so that the seemingly incessant tapping of the typewriter was an agitating aggravation.

Heaving a disgruntled sigh, she wandered down to the great room, past the sofa, where Georgia lay sprawled out asleep on the Navajo rug. With no appetite for breakfast, Katherine moved aimlessly around the room feeling uncharacteristically bored. Finally, Jason noticed her presence and glanced away from the typewriter over his shoulder, uttering a gruff, "Good morning," before turning around again.

"Morning," she murmured, trying futilely not to notice how his sun-bleached hair, still damp from his shower, curled slightly on the nape of his neck. She ached to touch him yet knowing she didn't dare, she hastily turned to the ceiling-high bookcase, scanning the titles, hoping to find something interesting to read that would occupy her thoughts for a while. Unusually, none of the titles appealed to her and she suddenly felt more discontent and bored than she had ever felt before in her entire life. She hid a yawn behind her hand, then stretched lazily, crossing her arms behind her head then extending them as far above her as she could reach as she tried to ease some of the tension that gripped her body. It was in that ridiculous position that Jason found her as he turned abruptly. Katherine froze, nearly hypnotized by the change in his expression. Gone was all the former aloofness. As his gaze swept over her, his features relaxed momentarily. Even his finely chiseled mouth altered slightly. Suddenly the fuller lower lip seemed more sensuously carved.

A slight movement by him alerted her to a danger she didn't fully understand but respected nonetheless. Blushing scarlet, she dropped her arms down to her sides again, tugging at the bottom of her halter that had hiked up during her stretching exercise. "Wh—what are you typing?" she asked breathlessly, not quite able to meet his intent gaze. Forcing herself to take a few steps toward him, she was able to see that the paper in the typewriter appeared to contain something that looked like notes. Smiling rather uncertainly, she nodded in the typewriter's direction. "What are you doing? Setting down an unbeatable system for winning at high-stakes poker?"

"Something like that," he murmured, still gazing at her relentlessly. Turning in his swivel chair to face her, he leaned back, clasping his arms round the back of his head. "Another rainy day," he commented idly, his expression becoming remote again. "What do you plan to do with yourself?"

Katherine clasped her hands together in front of her, lifting her shoulders in a slight shrug. "I don't really know." She sighed disgruntedly. "I just feel so . . . so restless. Do you ever feel that way?"

"Sometimes," he answered expressionlessly. "Everybody does."

"But when you get that way, I guess you just pack up

and move on to another gambling resort somewhere," Katherine said, not recognizing the exasperated glint that flared in his eyes until it was too late.

"You can't cure restlessness by changing locales," he said, his jaw tight. "Usually our discontent comes from within us, not from our surroundings." At her surprised look, he smiled sardonically. "What's wrong? Did you assume we gamblers never have deep thoughts, that we never consider anything beyond our next poker game?"

Katherine hastily shook her head, gesturing weakly. "No, I didn't assume . . ."

"Of course you did," he interrupted curtly, turning his back to her again. Without another word, he began typing once more.

Katherine really felt miserable now. She hadn't meant to irritate him. There was enough tension between them anyhow. The last thing she wanted to do was to add more strain to their already uneasy relationship. Gathering up all her courage, she went to stand beside him. "I-I can type fairly well," she said hesitantly, trying to smile. "I'd be glad to help you with this."

"I prefer doing it myself," was his brusque reply.

The obvious rebuff hurt and Katherine moved away, walking to where Georgia slept on the rug. Despite all Katherine's overtures, the dog only opened her eyes a couple of times, much more interested in continuing her nap than she was in play.

"Gosh, she sure is lazy when it rains," Katherine commented aloud, rising up from her knees to go stare out the window at the rain-drenched landscape. In the gray of the day, the woods were darker, the foliage lusher and a deeper green. A gentle wind jostled the heavy boughs of the pines and cedars, scattering crystalline drops of rain down onto the needle-carpeted ground. She tapped her fingernails against the windowpanes, her restlessness mounting steadily. "When's the sun supposed to shine again?" she asked, turning to face the room once more. "Have you heard the weather report?" When Jason continued typing, only shaking his head in answer, she wandered past the dog again, nudging her firm black nose with her bare toes. Georgia didn't stir. Katherine sighed, more audibly than she meant to. Yet Jason didn't even seem to notice that obvious signal of her discontent.

He did cease in his typing for a moment, however. Leaning back in the leather swivel chair, he raked long fingers through the thick swathe of hair that brushed his forehead, as if he were deep in thought.

Katherine watched him, her heartbeat quickening as he clasped his hands behind his head and the muscles of his broad shoulders rippled beneath the cotton knit fabric of his cream-colored rugby-styled shirt. Why did he always have to look so attractive and irresistibly virile that she could never see him without longing to feel the smooth tautness of his bronze skin beneath her fingertips again? It was insane that she had fallen in love with him in the first place. He was exactly what she had never wanted a man to be, yet she wanted him, more than she had ever wanted anything in her life. Frustrated by the ongoing battle of conflicting emotions within her, she dragged her gaze away from him.

"Want some coffee?" she asked softly, for lack of anything better to say. "I'd be glad to make some."

"No, thanks," he muttered shortly, resuming his work at the typewriter. "I already had four cups this morning. I think that's enough."

Unwisely choosing to ignore the trace of impatience in his voice, she went to lounge back against the roll-top desk beside the typing table. Crossing her long shapely legs at her ankles, she lifted her eyebrows questioningly. "Why did you need four cups of coffee to wake up this morning? You didn't get home all that late last night."

Cursing explicitly when he hit several wrong keys, Jason

stopped typing, raising his head to look at her, his steel blue eyes glinting. "Checking up on me?" he questioned sharply. "Maybe I should start signing in and out like freshman girls in college dorms have to do."

At his harsh tone, Katherine caught her upper lip between her teeth. She had never seen him in a mood like this. Either he was typing something very important or he was angry at her for some reason and fearing anger had prompted his sarcasm, she shook her head. "I wasn't checking on you," she murmured, her eyes deep dark pools of green. "I—I just happened to still be awake when you came in." When he only continued to stare at her almost broodingly, she quickly looked away, gesturing hesitantly, "Well, maybe it's too muggy and hot for coffee. So how about some iced tea or lemonade?"

"No. I don't want iced tea; I don't want lemonade," he answered, a muscle ticking in his jaw. "I wouldn't mind having a drink right now, but if I do, it'll be something considerably stronger than coffee, tea, or lemonade, I assure you."

"But it's only ten in the morning." Katherine frowned bewilderedly. "You never drink a lot so why would you want to start so early in the day?"

"Why?" he repeated mockingly, piercing eyes raking over her. "For heaven's sake, Kit, you could drive any man to drink at dawn."

"Me?" she exclaimed softly. "I don't know what you mean. Why should anyone want to drink because of me?"

Jason stood also, towering above her, his hands thrust deeply into the pockets of his navy trousers. Narrowed eyes, glittering dangerously, surveyed her for a long tense moment. Then, amazingly, he put out his right hand and ran it lightly over her slender left thigh, smiling mockingly when she trembled violently and jerked herself upright to stand staring up at him wide eyed. "You're such a little girl sometimes. You really don't know how you could drive a man to drink, do you? So I'd better tell you how. I could use a calming drink right now because you're wandering around here in those Daisy Mae shorts and that skimpy little halter. And when you entice me by occasionally stretching like a lazy little kitten, you can't expect me to keep my mind on what I'm doing. You obviously don't understand exactly what I'd like to be doing with you right now. It's a quiet, rainy day, Kit, and I'd very much enjoy spending all of it in my bed with you. Now, do you understand?"

Katherine's cheeks bloomed with entrancing rose color as her legs suddenly went weak beneath her. Nearly mesmerized by the passionate gaze that seemed to envelop her in its warm promise, she couldn't even shake her head. But at last she stammered an apologetic denial. "I didn't . . . Jason, I didn't mean to . . ."

"If you could only see yourself," he nearly growled, taking one step closer to her. "You're so inexperienced you really don't realize what kind of effect you have on me, do you? You may look every inch a woman but you're as innocent as a child. And you make me feel like a cad for wanting to make love to you."

Katherine's small chin jutted out in defiance. "I'm not *that* innocent," she protested heatedly. "And I'm certainly not a child."

"Prove it," he countered, lifting his hand as if to touch her again, then letting it drop. He heaved a sigh, massaging the nape of his neck wearily. "Just sit down somewhere and give me a moment's peace. I have work to do."

"Well, excuse me for living," she muttered petulantly, flouncing past him to subside in a huff on the sofa. Her green eyes glittered, challenging him as he watched her for a long moment, but when he shrugged at last and sat down at the typewriter again, her shoulders slumped. Her expression grew pensive as she stared intently at his broad back. This situation was crazy. He seemed to want her as much as she wanted him and for a fraction of a second, she wished she hadn't imposed such a strict code of morals on herself. If only she had the courage to drift into an intimate relationship with him, then at least she would know what it was like to give herself to the man she loved. Yet, even as she wished she could be different, she knew she wouldn't change. She would never be completely happy in an intimate relationship that wasn't also a lasting commitment but Jason wasn't the kind of man to make commitments. So, it was a stalemate.

Wrapping her arms across her chest, she stared down at Georgia. The dog sighed heavily in her sleep and turned over onto her back, thrusting one gangling leg straight up in the air. "How can she sleep in that crazy position?" Katherine muttered aloud. When Jason only mumbled something incomprehensible in response, she got up and wandered back to the floor-to-ceiling bookcase. She chose a pictorial history of Nevada, a heavy volume which slipped right through her fingers and crashed with a resounding bang onto the hardwood floor.

"Clumsy oaf," she whispered furiously, bending over to pick up the book. When she straightened again, she found Jason's darkening gaze drifting slowly upward along the slender length of her legs over the gentle curve of her hips, along the inward arching of her waist to the enticing hint of the shadowed hollow between her breasts revealed in the vee-neck of her halter. For a breathtaking moment, his eyes lingered there, then moved upward to meet hers.

"Are you being deliberately provocative, Kit?" he murmured, his voice deep and husky. With lithe ease of movement, he reached out and caught her wrist in one large hand, drawing her resolutely between his legs. His hands spanned her waist, his fingers brushing and caressing the sensitive skin of her bare midriff as he pulled her down to sit on one muscular thigh.

Her breath caught in her throat; her hands clutched the knit fabric of his sleeves as he traced a light fingertip along the neckline of her halter. When he lowered his head, his firm lips following the same path as his fingertip, a tremor of excitement trickled along her spine, awakening an empty aching inside her and almost of their own volition, her hands moved up to link behind his neck. She wanted his kiss more than she had ever wanted anything, but he didn't kiss her. Instead, he lifted his head again, capturing her bemused gaze in the stormy blue depths of his eyes.

"Is that it, Kit? Are you inviting me to take you up to my bed and make love to you?"

Though she longed to say yes, the remnants of her sanity wouldn't allow her to. Unhappily, she shook her head.

His pulse beat rapidly in his temples. A slight strained smile curved his lips. "No, I didn't think you really meant to be issuing an invitation," he said, his voice deceptively soft. Then without warning, he stood her on her feet and put her from him almost roughly. His expression became grim. "So, settle down somewhere and stop flitting around here in that provocative outfit. Read a book; play with the puppy; take a nap on the sofa. Just do something and stop distracting me. Please."

Scarlet color flared in her cheeks and she lowered her eyes. "I'm sorry."

Jason turned away. "Just go sit down, Kit."

She went and sat. After five minutes of staring at the implacable line of his back, however, she waited for a lull in his seemingly incessant typing. When silence finally came, she sat up straight on the sofa, declaring tersely, "I seem to be getting in your way here. So if your grumpiness this morning is a hint for me to get out, I'll leave. I can book a room in a hotel."

Muttering impatiently, Jason turned to glare at her. "I

rarely hint, Kit. If I wanted you to leave, I'd say so. So stop jumping to conclusions and shut up so I can get this work done."

Defensive anger erupted in Katherine and she jumped to her feet, glaring right back at him. "You're in a rotten mood today," she declared forcefully. "And I don't have to sit here and let you pick on me. I'm going for a walk. Maybe you'll be nicer when I come back."

"Take your raincoat," he calmly called after her as she marched into the foyer to the closet. "And I may not be here at all when you come back. There's a big game starting this afternoon. I don't want to miss it."

"Good," she snapped back at him, yanking her grass-green plastic raincoat from a hanger and grabbing her white vinyl rain hat. "And don't think you need to hurry home on my account. I do just fine here, all by myself."

"I'm glad to hear it," he replied laconically, a maddening note of amusement in his deep voice. "So I'll probably not see you until tomorrow. Have a nice walk."

Too incensed to think of a cutting retort, Katherine went out the front door, closing it forcefully behind her before he could say anything else.

She walked through the rain-soaked woods to her father's house, knowing he wouldn't be there and hoping Wendi wouldn't be either. It was Mallie she wanted to see, needed to talk to, because Mallie represented a semblance of security and at the moment, Katherine very much needed to feel secure with someone, somewhere.

Katherine found Mallie in the kitchen getting a head start on dinner. Offering to help, she sat down at the wooden worktable and began stuffing green peppers with a mixture of ground round beef, rice, onion, and to add a bit of zest, a pinch of chopped basil leaves. As she spooned this mixture into the fresh peppers, Mallie stood at the stove, keeping a close watch on her special tomato sauce that was simmering in a small pot.

"When are you going to tell me your secret recipe for that sauce?" Katherine asked. "Remember? You promised you'd give it to me when I grew up."

"I meant when you got married," Mallie answered without turning around. "So you'll have to wait awhile longer, I reckon. You're still too young to be trusted with my secret yet."

"Oh, for heaven's sake, everybody acts like I'm a two-year-old," Katherine protested irritably, still upset by her confrontation with Jason and certainly in no mood to be told by anyone else that she was too young for anything. Tucking her bare feet up beside her on her chair, she sighed impatiently. "But what if I don't ever get married? Will I still be too young for your secret recipe at age thirty? Thirty-five? Forty? I never realized before that a girl had to get married to be considered an adult."

Mallie chuckled. "Honey, you'll get married. I ain't got no doubts about that. Pretty as you are, some man soon's gonna scoop you up and never let go of you."

Katherine sniffed. "I'm not so sure I want to be 'scooped up.' I'm beginning to think all men are nothing more than sources of aggravation."

Turning from the stove, Mallie eyed her speculatively. "You sure got a bee in your bonnet today, ain't you?" she asked softly at last, wiping her work-roughened hands on the voluminous white apron she wore. She walked to the table and with a sigh, lowered her plump self down onto the chair across from Katherine. "I figured something was the matter when you got here. Your cheeks was just a mite too red."

"I nearly suffocated walking over here in that plastic raincoat. It's so muggy outside," Katherine said evasively. "That's why my cheeks were red. Nothing's the matter."

"You think I can't tell when something's bothering you?" Mallie asked, shaking her head chidingly. "Well, I can. I've known you since you was just a little thing and there's always been a certain look you get in your eyes when something's the matter. And that look was there when you got here awhile ago. So you might as well tell me what's bothering you. I'm betting it has something to do with that gambler you're living with. Has he been trying to force himself on you?"

Katherine had to smile, though rather bleakly, as she shook her head. "No, he hasn't been trying to force himself on me. Actually, I think he'd be quite happy to see me move out of his house, today, if possible."

"Well, you oughta move out," Mallie said very seriously. "It just ain't right for a young girl like you to be living in the same house with a man, especially since you got some real strong feelings for him." She raised a silencing hand when Katherine started to speak. "Ain't no use in trying to tell me you don't feel something for him, Kit. I ain't lived all these years for nothing. I can tell when somebody's in love."

"You're too perceptive," Katherine complained half-heartedly, but she squeezed the housekeeper's arm and smiled wanly. "But there's no use talking about this. Nitwit that I am, I've let myself fall in love with Jason, but he'll probably never take any relationship seriously and that's that."

"Then you oughta come home, Kit," Mallie persisted ominously. "Girls in love ain't always smart. Stay with this Jason Roarke and you just might get yourself too mixed-up with him. So stop being so stubborn and move on back here again."

Katherine shook her head with renewed obstinance. "I can't back down now. When my father starts acting sensibly, I'll come back and not before. My father . . ." Her words were interrupted abruptly by the loud bang of the front door being slammed. She and Mallie exchanged puzzled glances, then the housekeeper rose heavily to her feet. "Wonder what your daddy's doing back here so soon? He just left about an hour ago." Walking to the stove, she surveyed the potful of simmering sauce. "I got to stir this awhile. You go see what he forgot."

"Is Wendi here?" Katherine asked, wrinkling her nose distastefully. "I don't want to see her."

"She ain't got here yet. Probably sleeping late, as usual," Mallie said sharply. "Now, go on and see what Mr. Brice needs."

It was a command rather than a request, so Katherine went, although reluctantly. She had no desire to talk to her father right now or at any time, actually, until Wendi had left this house. Pausing by the door to his study, she took a deep fortifying breath, then ambled into the room, frowning slightly when she found Brice at the portable bar, pouring himself a drink.

"Mallie wants to know if you forgot something," Katherine said softly, drawing his attention. Then she tilted her head to one side inquiringly as she noticed the glint in his green eyes and the white line of strain outlining his lips. As he slouched down in an oversized brown leather chair, taking a generous swallow of his drink, she approached him. "Don't you feel well? Your skin looks a little peculiar, almost ashen."

"I'm okay," he answered curtly. Then he jerked up his head and glared at her. "Have you finally come to your senses and decided to move back in here where you belong?"

"No. And I don't plan to," she replied, glaring right back at him. "I told you I won't come back until . . ."

"I know what you told me," he interrupted harshly, swishing the amber-colored liquid in his glass. "And I told you I wouldn't be blackmailed. I'll live my life the way I please. No twenty-one-year-old slip of a girl is going to tell me what to do."

"Fine. And since I'm over eighteen, you can't tell me what to do, either," Katherine reminded him pithily. "So, I plan to stay with Jason."

"Don't be such a little fool, Kit," Brice said furiously, sitting up straight in his chair. "You don't want to mess up your life just to get back at me."

"Me! Mess up *my* life?" Katherine exclaimed softly. "What about you? Why do you want to get involved with a girl like Wendi when you could have a wonderful woman like Jess Whitney?"

"Could I?" Brice countered mockingly. "I think you overestimate Jess's feelings for me. You must, since I went into the office this morning and discovered she's left town."

"She's left?" Katherine exclaimed, sinking down onto the leather sofa that matched the chair. "When?"

"Last night, apparently." Brice raked his fingers through his hair, then loosened his tie with a weary disbelieving shake of his head. "It doesn't make sense that she didn't even discuss this with me. She just went. She did leave me a little note, saying she thought it was time for her to move on. Now, what kind of sense does that make?"

"It makes perfect sense to me," Katherine said, examining her fingernails intently. "Though I have to admit I'm surprised she actually left, even if she did tell me she was thinking about it."

"She told you! But she didn't talk to me about it?" Brice growled angrily. "She might have at least given me some notice, after working for me for ten years."

Katherine could hardly believe she had heard him correctly. "Is that all Jess was to you? An employee?"

Brice waved his hand in an impatient gesture. "Of course not. I thought she and I were friends but . . ."

"Friends? Don't you realize she's in love with you? That

she's been in love with you since that affair the two of you had ten years ago?"

It was Brice's turn to look surprised and very uncomfortable. "I didn't realize you knew about that."

"I realized Jess was in love with you and mentioned that to Mallie. She told me the rest."

"She had no right to do that," Brice muttered, one hand balling into a fist on the arm of the chair. "What Jess and I had together ended long ago."

"For you maybe. But not for her. She still loves you."

Brice grimaced disbelievingly. "She sure has a funny way of showing it—walking out on me this way."

"What do you care?" Katherine countered hotly, exasperated by his apparent selfishness. "Why should she stay here and watch you dallying with an endless parade of girls? I don't think Jess is a masochist and your affair with Wendi was the last straw. So she just left, but it certainly shouldn't matter to you. You don't love her."

"You're so quick to think the worst of me, Kit," he ground out resentfully, his eyes flashing green fire. "How can you be so sure I don't love Jess? Maybe I . . ." His words trailed off to silence as he glanced past Katherine toward the study door. Suddenly his face became an unreadable mask, showing no emotion whatsoever.

Curious, Katherine turned, her temper rising as she watched Wendi stroll into the room, peeling off her raincoat and tossing it carelessly onto a chair.

"Kit, it's wonderful to see you!" she declared, actually unwise enough to give the younger girl's shoulders a brief squeeze. Then she went to Brice and leaned down to kiss his mouth before she curled up on the arm of his chair, laying a possessive hand against his neck. She flashed Katherine a too-radiant smile.

"Brice and I were hoping you'd come soon," Wendi continued blithely, fluffing her dark hair with one lazily limp hand. She smiled down at the man as possessively as she was touching him, then looked at Katherine again, her eyes glinting slyly. "I know that you moved out because you felt your father and I might want to be alone here sometimes, but really, that was silly, wasn't it Brice? We want you here, Kit. Honest. I don't see why the three of us can't be one big happy family."

Katherine saw why they couldn't and she had had enough of this ridiculous conversation. At the best of times, Wendi was nearly impossible to tolerate, but now that she was trying to cast herself in the role of loving stepmother, Katherine couldn't bear to be around her another minute. "I have to go now," she mumbled, standing to thrust her hands into the pockets of her cut-off jeans. "I'll see you later. Unfortunately," she added beneath her breath as she started toward the door.

"I'll drive you," Brice called after. "It's raining too hard for you to walk all that way."

Katherine hesitated, then reluctantly turned as her father loosened Wendi's grip on him and stood also. "You don't need to drive me. I don't mind walking in the rain. Besides, I wore a raincoat and hat over here."

"But no shoes. I'm not letting you walk all the way back barefoot. And I don't mind driving you."

As he approached Katherine, she shook her head. "But . . ."

"I'm driving you and that's final," he declared authoritatively. "Now go get your coat."

"But Brice, darling," Wendi whined, her expression of displeasure adding years to her pixie-like face. "What about me? I thought you were home for the day. Now what am I going to do all by myself?"

"Go shopping. Again," he answered brusquely, taking out his wallet to hand her a generous number of bills. "I'm sure you can keep yourself occupied in the boutiques all day. And if you want to join me for dinner, you'd better come to the casino. I probably won't have time to come back here unless I get lucky today and find a secretary to replace Jess."

"Replace Jess! You mean she's quit?" Wendi crowed, then managed to control her elation to some extent. Though there was an unmistakable glint of triumph in her eyes, she arranged her face in suitably sober lines. "Oh, dear, and she was such a dependable secretary, wasn't she? I do hope you can find someone as efficient as she was to take her place."

Thoroughly disgusted by Wendi's hypocrisy, Katherine marched out of the study. After bidding Mallie good-bye, she donned her raincoat, then went outside to wait for her father in his Porsche. A few minutes later, he finally appeared, started the car, and drove out onto the narrow highway without saying a word. And Katherine said nothing to him. There was nothing she could say. It was impossible to talk intelligently with a man who'd choose a nincompoop like Wendi over a woman like Jess. The little respect Katherine had ever felt for her father abruptly shriveled and died. As she stared blindly out her window as they stopped before Jason's house, she blinked away the tears that were gathering in her eyes.

"Thanks for the ride," she murmured. But as she touched the door handle, Brice caught her left arm.

His expression was grim. "I don't want you staying here any longer, Kit," he muttered. "So stop being so stubborn and come home. You can't object that much to Wendi."

"Can't I?" Katherine countered mockingly, pulling her arm free. "Well, I do object to her. I can't stop you from making her my stepmother but . . ."

"Stepmother! I'm not about to make her your step-mother!"

"I don't think she knows that," Katherine said curtly. "Maybe you'd better tell her you don't plan to marry her so she'll stop putting on that loving stepmother act for me.

153

Better yet, stop seeing her! Then I'll come back. And if you really want to make me happy, go after Jess, bring her back here, and try to see that she's worth a million Wendi Millers."

"Don't you think I know that?" Brice nearly groaned. "But I think Jess is better off without me. In fact, she should have left a long time ago. I've never been the right man for her."

Katherine frowned. "What does that mean?"

Brice's smile was unpleasant and self derisive. "I mean I'm not husband material. Just ask your mother; she'll tell you. I've never been good at honoring personal commitments so Jess is better off without me."

Katherine stared at him, realizing for the first time that he really didn't like himself much. "You could change," she suggested softly. "You could honor your commitments if you really tried."

Smiling ruefully, Brice shook his head. "You can't teach an old dog new tricks, Kit. And Jess will be better off not trying."

Detecting the genuine regret and pain in his eyes, Katherine felt a surge of pity. "You love her, don't you? And you're afraid to let yourself? You know what, Daddy?" she whispered. "I think I feel sorry for you."

Brice looked startled for an instant, then resigned. "It's interesting," he muttered wearily. "You haven't called me Daddy since you were a little girl and now that you've finally said it again, you're telling me you feel sorry for me. There's something sad in that. Isn't there?"

"Yes. Very sad," she answered thickly. To avoid bursting into tears in front of him, she jumped out of the Porsche and dashed into Jason's house. Once inside, she leaned back against the door, massaging her temples, trying to sort out her jumbled thoughts. Just now, in her father's eyes, she had detected honest vulnerability. If Brice Delacorte could be vulnerable, she realized Jason could be vulnerable, too, but that possibility only made her love him more, which was the last thing she wanted to do.

A sharp clap of thunder awakened Katherine with such harsh abruptness that she sat up straight in bed. A jagged streak of lightning flashed across the black sky outside her window. Her heart, which had seemed to stop for an instant, began to thud violently with such irregular rhythm that she pressed her fist between her breasts as she tried to catch her breath. She hated storms. At least, she hated them when she had to endure them alone and she was alone tonight. Jason was undoubtedly still at his poker game, so except for the cowardly Georgia, Katherine had the house to herself. As a gusting wind whistled through the boughs of the tall trees, she rubbed her arms briskly, flinching as another jagged streak of lightning ripped the sky, illuminating her room eerily for an instant. Between bright flashes, the pitch blackness in the room unnerved her. She reached out toward the bedside table, but when she switched on the lamp, nothing happened.

"Oh, no," she whispered miserably, drawing her knees up close against her chest. Now that she knew the electricity was out, she was uneasy about being alone. Though she had never been absolutely terrified of the darkness, she didn't exactly relish it either, especially now, marooned in this isolated house, separated from the neighbors on each side by stands of trees. The storm continued its fierce assault. Rain lashed the windows; the lightning flashes split the sky too often and the thunder was too loud. Finally, after five minutes of sitting on the bed, Katherine knew she'd never get back to sleep again without some light to still her unreasonable fears. If only she had some candles, she thought wistfully, then suddenly remembered the kerosene lamp kept in the pantry downstairs for just such emergencies as this.

Lowering her bare feet to the cool hardwood floor, she got out of bed warily, tiptoeing to her door, though she had no idea why she wanted to be so quiet. Easing open the door, she peered into the dark hallway. Though she wasn't eager to make her way downstairs to the kitchen, she lacked any other alternative if she wanted a light. She moved across the hall cautiously, groping for the railing overlooking the great room. Knowing the newel post at the railing's end would indicate the exact location of the stairs, she walked on less timidly, much to her subsequent regret. As her hand bumped the newel post, her bare right foot came down on something soft and warm and yielding. Katherine uttered a little cry and in the split second she realized she was about to trod on Georgia, she tried to miss the dog by twisting her body to one side. In the process, she landed down hard on the side of her right foot, wrenching her ankle. She fell, barely saving herself from a tumble down the steps by catching hold of the newel post. She landed with a thump on her thigh and elbow at the very edge of the stairway. Pain pierced through her ankle, radiating up to her calf and down to her toes. Katherine bit down hard on her lower lip as Georgia tried to lick her cheeks, whimpering confusedly.

"Silly animal. The head of the stairs is no place to sleep," Katherine chided halfheartedly, stroking the dog in an effort to calm her. "Stop wiggling or you'll push me down the steps."

Miraculously, Georgia obeyed but only because a noise in the hallway behind them captured her attention. With one massive paw still on Katherine's thigh, the dog jerked her golden head around toward Jason's bedroom then stood perfectly still. Katherine's breath caught on a startled gasp as a beam of light was suddenly directed right at her face, blinding her.

"Kit, are you okay?" Jason's deep voice came out of the darkness.

Relief rushed through Katherine, leaving her weak and trembling. "Thank heaven, it's you," she uttered squeakily as Jason directed the light away from her face. When he came and knelt down beside her, she took a deep shuddering breath. "For a second, I thought you might be an intruder. I–I didn't think you'd come home tonight."

"The game ended sooner than I expected," he said, gripping her waist to help her sit up. After exiling the wriggling dog to the corner with a no-nonsense command, he turned his attention back to Katherine again. "What happened, Kit?"

She explained the accident, then laughed self-consciously. "Sometimes I think Georgia is out to get me. First she attacked me on the beach and now this."

Silhouetted in the beam of the flashlight behind him, Jason shook his head. "The two of you together do seem a little accident-prone. Now, are you hurt or just shaken up a bit?"

She wanted to lie but as she tried to raise her right knee, the pain that gripped her ankle compelled her to gasp out the truth, "I think I've sprained my right ankle. It hurts like the devil."

Gentle fingertips probed the throbbing flesh surrounding her ankle. When she drew in a sharp breath, he swiftly gathered her up in his strong arms and stood effortlessly. With one foot, he pushed the flashlight around on the floor so that its beam illuminated the open doorway to her room.

Katherine lay quietly against his bare, hair-roughened chest but her pulses began to race. Her ankle was nearly forgotten and she gazed bemusedly up at him as he put her down gently on her bed in the semi-darkness.

"I'll have to take the flashlight for a minute," he said softly. "I'll get the kerosene lamp from my room so we can take a closer look at that ankle."

As Katherine watched him stride out her door, she

noticed with a lurch of her heart how his dark pajama pants hung low on his lean hips. She had seen him in pajamas before when he had been sick but somehow tonight was different. It was as if the electrical forces of the storm were concentrating in her room and an incredibly intense excitement rose in her.

Jason, however, appeared cool and composed as he returned with the first-aid kit and the lamp, which bathed the room in soft illumination. Sitting down on the edge of the bed, he was impersonal and methodical as he lightly probed the swelling tissue below her ankle. "Seems like a sprain," he pronounced. "You'll have to get it X-rayed tomorrow to be sure though. I'll wrap it for now unless you think I should just take you to the hospital."

Katherine hastily shook her head. "Oh, no; I'm sure it's only sprained."

"I hope so," he murmured, beginning to wrap the bandage beneath her instep, drawing it up over her foot, then over and behind her ankle in the classic figure eight. He paused a moment, glancing at her. "What were you doing out in the hall?"

She smiled sheepishly. "I wanted the lamp from downstairs so I could get back to sleep."

His hands were still again as his dark blue eyes searched her face. "Are you afraid of the dark, Kit?" he inquired softly. "I thought only gamblers frightened you."

Unable to interpret his enigmatic expression, she couldn't be sure if he was teasing her or being serious. So she never answered him.

After securing the metal-pronged fastener of the bandage into the elastic fabric, Jason allowed his narrowing gaze to trail slowly up the long length of Katherine's creamy bare legs.

She shifted nervously, realizing how little she was wearing. Her white cotton camisole and matching tap pants were cool but sheer, a fact that Jason seemed to be realizing, too, at that very moment. Scarcely able to breathe, she sat immobile against her propped-up pillow as his dark eyes drifted upward to linger on the rounded contours of her breasts. Then his large brown hands feathered over her slender legs, his thumbs brushing the sensitive skin of her inner thighs. Katherine gasped softly, her heart pounding with dizzying rapidity as his hands continued their searching journey over her abdomen to span her insweeping waist. Effortlessly and with great finesse, he moved her so that she was lying on the bed.

"Kit," he whispered roughly, sliding one arm beneath her shoulders as he came down beside her. His fingers tangled in the thick hair at her nape, holding her fast as he lowered his head. His firm mouth brushed against hers with evocative lightness, then he drew away slightly.

She gazed up at him, her softly bemused eyes captured and held within the azure depths of his. "Oh, Jason," she whispered back, tentatively lifting her slender arms to rest across his shoulders. As her fingertips grazed the strong brown column of his neck, his lean features tightened. Passion blazed in his eyes. With her sharp intake of breath her lips parted and his descended to possess her mouth with a hunger tempered by a devastating touch of tenderness. The fierce taking power of his kiss ignited her own smoldering desires. A pulsating thrill rippled deep within her, awakening an aching emptiness she knew only he could assuage. Caught up in a world where only the two of them existed, she tightened her arms round his broad shoulders, urging him nearer. Delighted, half-frightened, yet eager all at once as he bore her down into the soft mattress, she trembled as one muscular thigh parted hers slightly. His lips explored hers, exerting a light twisting pressure that opened her mouth to the tongue that tasted her own.

Her senses spiraled as he tugged at the ribbon closures of her camisole, then pushed the cotton fabric aside, exposing the cushioned roundness of her breasts to his seeking touch. His fingers grazed over her firm silken flesh, probing, caressing, conveying barely restrained desires. Strong teeth gently nibbled her earlobe as his thumbs brushed the rosette peaks, arousing them to throbbing hardness. Then he lowered his mouth to the shadowed scented hollow between her breasts. He tasted each straining nipple, tantalizing her with the moist roughness of his tongue. The sensations he aroused made her moan softly and arch against him. As he turned onto his side, taking her with him, and his hard arms encircled her slender young body, she yielded eagerly to his superior strength.

"We both knew this had to happen," he muttered huskily, his lips trailing across her cheek. "Didn't we, Kit?"

Perhaps she had known. Perhaps, subconsciously, she had moved into his house, hoping it would happen. Perhaps teaching her father a lesson had only been a suitable excuse. Katherine didn't know. At the moment, she was beyond rational thought, too enthralled by Jason's nearness to analyze her motives for moving in with him. All she wanted now was for him to go on touching her and she conveyed that need by moving evocatively against the long length of his body.

Jason made no attempt to hide his response. His hands spread open over the soft curve of her hips and the hard ridge of his body surged powerfully against her abdomen. Ages-old feminine instinct compelled her to press closer to him. Her trembling fingers explored the heated flesh of his muscular back. Her hands stroked his lean sides as he whispered her name hoarsely, and her breathless sigh signaled total submission.

"I won't hurt you," he promised, taking her mouth with a tender strength that proved his words.

But as his long, hard legs tangled with hers, his calf

brushed her injured ankle, jarring it. Katherine tensed involuntarily with the pain, then murmured in protest as he pulled away slightly.

"What am I doing?" he groaned, dragging his arms from around her, stilling her hands as they sought to keep him close. "Kit, I can't make love to you this way. You're afraid."

"No. I'm not. You just nudged my ankle. I . . ." She was silenced as she opened her eyes and saw the grim expression on his face. Yet, as he lowered his feet to the floor and stood, she reached out to catch his large wrist, her green eyes pleading with him to stay. "Don't leave me," she whispered. "I'm not afraid. I want you to . . ."

"You want me tonight, Kit," he muttered gruffly, easily removing her small fingers from his wrist. He shook his head, the hot light in his blue eyes piercing the soft depths of hers. "But what about afterward? What about tomorrow morning? You'll tell yourself I just used you. You don't trust me, Kit, and I don't want to make you hate me."

Pressing her fingers against her lips, Katherine watched him turn and walk out her door. She longed to call out and tell him that she *did* trust him. But she couldn't, because she didn't.

Chapter Ten

The next morning, Jason's housekeeper, Mary, was dusting the furniture in the great room when Katherine hobbled down the stairs. A plump little woman in her late forties, Mary smiled pleasantly, then proceeded to flick one last imaginary piece of dust from the mahogany bar next to the staircase. Katherine limped across the room to rest one hand on the back of the sofa, taking some of the weight off her ankle. Hesitantly calling Mary's name when the maid started toward the kitchen, she asked softly, "Where is . . . Has Mr. Roarke left?"

"Just stepped outside for a breath of fresh air," Mary informed her cheerily. "Be back in a minute or two, I guess. Are you 'bout ready for some breakfast, Miss Delacorte?"

Katherine shook her head. "Thanks, but I'm not very hungry."

"Coffee then?"

"Maybe later. But I can get that myself. I won't have to interrupt your cleaning."

"Whatever you say, miss," Mary agreed. After flashing Katherine another genuinely friendly smile, she headed for the kitchen.

Alone, Katherine hobbled around the sofa to sit down close to the armrest where she heaved a long dejected sigh and stared pensively at the cold stone fireplace. Lack of sleep made her eyes feel positively gritty and she closed them wearily, wishing she didn't feel so confused. She wanted to see Jason this morning; yet, she didn't. Last night's events had been very bewildering. Though she had been eager for Jason to make love to her, he hadn't taken what she was so willing to give, saying he knew she would regret it afterward. He had wanted her; she knew that, which made his honorable consideration of her feelings all the more confusing. His behavior was so rarely what she expected a gambler's behavior would be; he seemed more than anything like a puzzle with some of the pieces missing and she simply couldn't understand him, though she longed to. She wanted to trust him, but her feelings for her father and the kind of life he led were too deeply ingrained in her; it seemed impossible that she could put her faith in any man even remotely like him.

Resting her head back, she sighed again, but her eyes flew open and she sat up straight when she heard the front door open, then close again immediately. Her stomach fluttered as she peeked around the back of the sofa, smiling shyly when Jason looked up and noticed her there. In a black crew-neck sweater and black trousers, he was too disturbingly attractive and the mere sight of him evoked memories of how he had made her feel last night. Hoping to mask her response, she tried to smile demurely up at him as he came to stand beside her.

"The rain cooled things off a little," she said, then berated herself for uttering such an insipid statement.

Jason only nodded, then frowned. "Why are you sitting there like that?" he asked, reaching across her to pick up two of the throw pillows on the sofa. "You should have that ankle elevated, Kit. And don't walk on it any more than you have to until it's been X-rayed. I thought I'd drive you over to the hospital this morning."

"Oh, but you don't have to go to all that trouble," Katherine protested weakly as he knelt on the floor in front of her and lifted her right foot. His touch was impersonal as he lowered her heel to the stacked pillows on the coffee table yet the brushing of his fingertips across the bare skin above the bandage sent a shiver along her spine. She swallowed uneasily. "I can call Mallie and have her drive me to the hospital, if you really think it's necessary. I mean, I'm sure my ankle's only sprained."

"It's necessary," he pronounced dictatorially, rising to his feet again. "And I'll take you to have it X-rayed. That way I'll be certain you really have one taken."

There was something in his tone that Katherine didn't care for and she lifted her chin defensively. "You sound as if you don't trust me."

"Well, that makes us even, doesn't it? We both know you don't trust me."

His words recalled last night and suddenly erected a wall between them that Katherine had no idea how to breach. She dragged her gaze away from the dark intensity of his to stare morosely at her injured limb. If only she could have freed herself of all inhibition and thrown herself into his arms, she would have done so in that moment, but the cautious behavior of a lifetime couldn't be eradicated so easily. Sensing he was still watching her, she glanced up and almost flinched as she met the brooding look in his dark blue eyes. At last he turned away and she could breathe again, but an oppressive heaviness seemed to drag at her limbs. She had never felt so lost and confused in her life. How had she gotten herself into this mess? Other girls fell in love, were loved in return, and everything was easy. Why was she so different? She had expected to find a dependable man with whom love could come slowly and comfortably. In her wildest imaginings, she had never dreamed a man like Jason could arouse in her such a tumultuous intermingling of emotions—love, begrudging respect, and, most disturbing of all, the irrepressible desire to belong to him. She had gone out with other young attractive men and often she had wondered if she might be frigid because their kisses hadn't excited her at all. But Jason had proven beyond a shadow of doubt that she was not frigid.

Why had he been the man who awakened all her latent sexuality, she wondered bleakly, watching as he unlocked his roll-top desk and removed a sheaf of papers from it. As he sat down in his leather swivel chair, stretching his long legs out in front of him, she found herself staring at the muscular lineation of his thighs straining against the tautened fabric of his trousers. Her gaze trailed slowly upward over the flat hard abdomen and broad strong chest to the chiselled features of his tan face. She loved him so completely and she was so miserable. Suddenly, he looked up, his jaw tightening and a strange light flaring in his narrowing eyes as they met hers.

"Kit," he muttered roughly, moving as if he meant to stand. "This is insane. We have to . . ." A knock on the front door interrupted him and with an explicit curse, he lithely rose to his feet. As he walked past Katherine, he paused a moment and laid his hand against the thickness of her auburn hair. No words accompanied this exquisitely tender gesture, but there was unmistakable regret in his expression as he dropped his hand and continued on to the door.

It was Brice who came into the great room, frowning when he saw his daughter's bandaged ankle. "What happened to you?"

"Would you believe I tripped over a dog in the dark?"

"He would if he'd ever seen Georgia," Jason interceded wryly, only the faint glimmer in his eyes indicating that Brice had interrupted the beginning of a serious conversation. With a hint of a smile, he explained about Georgia. "She's a rather gangling, clumsy Labrador and when she and Kit get together, they somehow manage to get into some sort of tangle."

"She's just a puppy, though," Katherine felt compelled to defend the dog, then herself. "And it's not all my fault. She and I are always bumping into each other."

"I don't recall blaming you," Jason retorted, his tone almost teasing. "It's just inevitable that you and Georgia fall over each other often. Both of you are very young."

Katherine wrinkled her nose at him, then blushed slightly as she noticed her father's speculative gaze drift from Jason to her then back to Jason again, as if he didn't know what to think of their bantering exchange. Shifting uncomfortably on the sofa, she patted the cushion beside her. "Sit down," she said softly, wondering why he had come, yet hating to ask outright. So she exercised diplomacy. "I'm a little surprised to see you here."

"I imagine you are," Brice responded, giving her one of those crooked hesitant smiles. "But after our conversation yesterday, I started thinking about what you'd said. And . . . well, the fact of the matter is, I've told Wendi it's all over between us."

Katherine was too astounded to speak. She had believed her father's obstinacy exceeded even her own and though she had moved in with Jason in the hope that Brice would drop Wendi, lately she had begun to have doubts that her ploy would work. She had no idea what she had said to him yesterday that could have influenced him in any way; he had never before shown an inclination to respect her opinions.

"I thought you'd be happy to hear my news," Brice

commented as she simply stared at him. "Don't you have anything to say?"

"I'm just so surprised," Katherine explained softly. "What did I say yesterday that made you change your mind?"

Brice withdrew a pack of cigarettes from his pocket, took one out and lit it, then inhaled deeply. His expression was very serious. "Maybe it was what you said about Wendi trying to act like a stepmother to you. I began to realize she did seem to be getting ideas in that direction so I decided I'd better just tell her I'd no longer be paying her hotel bill for her."

"I don't imagine she was too pleased."

Smiling ruefully, Brice shook his head. "At first, she tried crying, swearing she had nowhere to go. But when she saw I meant what I said, she proceeded to call me every dirty name she could think of."

"Where *will* she go?" Katherine asked, feeling some pity for the girl, though she was a rather unpleasant person. "From what she told me, she had absolutely no money."

"She has money now," Brice said dryly. "And I also called a friend of mine in Las Vegas. He said he might be able to book her for a short singing engagement. So that placated her somewhat."

"Well, now that you've gotten rid of her, will you try to get Jess to come back?" was Katherine's next question. But she almost regretted her bluntness when her father's face lost all expression. Impulsively, she laid her hand on his arm. "You do want Jess back, don't you?"

"That has nothing to do with anything," he answered tersely. "She left of her own free will. I certainly won't chase after her and beg her to come back."

Katherine breathed an exasperated sigh. "You are the most stubborn human being I have . . ."

"I came over today to tell you that Wendi is leaving

Tahoe," Brice interrupted imperiously. "So there's no need for you to stay here any longer. You've gotten what you wanted, so you can come home."

Until that moment, Katherine hadn't stopped to consider what Wendi's leaving would mean to her. She would have to leave Jason's because there was no longer any excuse to stay. Suddenly, she realized she didn't want to go, though staying here in the same house with him had made a shambles of her nerves and even had been potentially dangerous. But at least she had been able to see him every day. Despite all the tensions between them, there had been many moments when they had simply sat and talked and she would miss those quiet times almost as much as she missed the excitement he could generate in her by merely touching her hand. She looked up at him. He hadn't sat down again since Brice had arrived. Leaning against the built-in bar along the staircase, his hands thrust into his pockets, he returned her look unwaveringly, his eyes as unreadable as they had been the few times she'd seen him play poker. What was he thinking? Was he relieved that she would finally be leaving? Katherine didn't have any idea what was running through his mind. Finally, she realized her father was watching her expectantly and she reluctantly turned her attention to him.

"When will Wendi be going?" she asked, hoping for a reprieve of at least two or three days.

Brice's answer was a disappointment, however. "She's packing right now. There's an eleven-fifty flight to Las Vegas and Mallie said she'd be delighted to drive Wendi to the airport." Brice smiled wryly. "I didn't even have to ask her to play chauffeur. She volunteered. So you go get packed now, Kit, and come home with me."

"I'd planned to take Kit to the hospital to have her ankle X-rayed," Jason interceded, speaking for the first time in several minutes. "It would be a wise precaution to take. Her ankle could be broken. I don't think it is, but it could be, so if you're busy, Brice, I'll go ahead and take her."

"I'll take her myself," Brice answered almost irritably, his tone indicating a hint of paternal possessiveness. "Kit's my responsibility." Not yours, he seemed to be adding silently.

Though there was a glimmer of reaction in Jason's eyes, he smiled, but the smile was somewhat mocking. "Whatever you want to do, Brice."

This new undercurrent of tension did nothing positive for Katherine's already frazzled nerves. Gingerly lowering her foot to the floor, she stood clumsily, unable to look directly at either her father or Jason. "I'll go pack," she murmured. "It won't take long."

Before she could attempt to take a step, Jason was beside her, sweeping her up in his arms with an unabashed smile. "Didn't I tell you not to walk unless it was absolutely necessary?"

Katherine nodded bemusedly as he carried her to the stairs and started up to her room, but with every step he took she was aware that her father was boring holes through both of them with a disapproving glare. That didn't seem to matter much, however, when Jason crossed the threshold of her room and kicked the door shut behind them.

Her startled expression elicited his most irresistible indulgent smile. "Yes, I know Brice is probably mad right now because I'm in your bedroom with you and the door's closed, but he'll just have to tolerate it since I need to talk to you."

"You do?" she whispered breathlessly, her senses spinning as she inhaled the familiar lime fragrance of his aftershave.

"I do," he whispered back, stopping in the center of the

169

room, still cradling her in his arms. His narrowed gaze trailed along the lissome slenderness of her body. "Kit, I'm going to miss you, but I think it's better for you to go home with your father. Don't you?"

"Why" she asked, unaware of the sad downward curve of her lips. "I mean, why do you think it's best? Have I been that much of a nuisance to you?"

"Not a nuisance, Kit. A temptation," he answered softly, captivating her with the drowsy cadence of his deep voice. "And after what almost happened last night, I know I wouldn't be able to resist that temptation much longer if you stayed here."

A becoming rose color tinted Katherine's cheeks. "Oh, Jason, I . . ." She was silenced as he lowered his head to cover her mouth with a gentle feather-light kiss and his lips hardened only slightly in demand as her arms around his neck tightened. He lifted his head again, a glimmer of barely restrained passion in his eyes seemingly willing her to lose herself in the deep dark blue pools. "I think we could start all over again if I don't have to cope with knowing you're sleeping in the room next to mine every night. And I do intend to begin again with you. So I'll be seeing you. Often."

"But why?" Katherine exclaimed softly, suspiciously. "You're not *really* interested in me. You couldn't be. You spent the night with Julie."

He frowned slightly, apparently confused. Then understanding narrowed his eyes and at last he shook his head. "I didn't spend the night with Julie, Kit. I spent the other night in a hotel because I didn't trust myself to stay here with you. So you're very wrong in thinking I'm not interested in you." He put her down gently on the edge of the bed, pressing one light fingertip against her lips when she started to speak. "Just sit there. Stay off that ankle. I'll send Mary up to help you pack." His finger trailed downward from her mouth to beneath her chin, tilting her face up. He leaned down to kiss her again, his firm lips moving gently and too fleetingly over the soft shape of hers. Then he straightened and left the room.

Katherine lifted trembling fingers to touch her lips. A soft, agonized moan escaped her. Jason was driving her crazy. Though she longed to believe he was seriously interested in her, she knew that couldn't be true. Some gambling men could charm the birds right out of the trees, Mallie had said, and now Katherine believed it. And to make matters worse, she was almost to the point where she wished she could simply succumb to Jason's charm and allow herself to be seduced.

True to his word, Jason did visit Katherine. Three days after she had left his house, he came to see her. The sun was setting, turning the surface of the lake to shimmering gold and tinting the western sky orange. Katherine sat on the beach, chin resting on her drawn-up knees, allowing her mind to drift to implausible fantasies as she gazed bemusedly at the exquisite sunset.

As she felt warm hands descend on her shoulders and Jason's deep voice softly saying her name, it was as if her fantasies were coming true. He sat down behind her on the blanket, lifting her hair forward over one shoulder. His lips grazed the sensitive skin of her nape, but when she would have instinctively turned into his arms, he stilled her movement, encircling her waist to draw her back against him.

He said nothing and as Katherine began to relax, her head came to rest in the hollow of his shoulder as he brushed wayward strands of hair back from her cheeks. It was the oddest sensation, being held by him this way. Since he had joined her on the blanket, she had only glimpsed his face and he hadn't kissed her at all except for the light touch of his lips on her nape. She felt content, strangely secure, and she realized with some surprise that if he only wanted her physically and this was his method of seducing her, then seduction was sweet.

Long lazy minutes passed as the sun sank lower behind the Sierra ranges bordering the opposite shore. For the first time in weeks, Katherine was free of real tension but, unfortunately, peace was short-lived. As she laid her own hands over Jason's, inviting the tightening of his muscular arms around her slim waist, Brice appeared beside them, his glowering glance at Jason shattering the tranquillity.

"Kit, I want to talk to you," he commanded rather than requested.

Diplomatically, Jason pulled his arms, with obvious reluctance, from around Katherine's waist and stood, then discreetly walked away toward the water's edge.

"What is it?" Katherine asked worriedly as Brice came down on his heels beside her. "Is something wrong?"

"I know where Jess is," he announced unceremoniously. "She applied for a job in L.A. and someone from personnel called me to check her references. I got her address by lying and saying I had a bonus check to send her."

"And?" Katherine questioned expectantly. "What do you plan to do now? Are you still too stubborn to go after her or have you changed your mind?"

"I've changed my mind," Brice admitted gruffly. "I miss her. I guess I'm just one of those dopes who didn't know what he had until he lost it."

"I guess you are," Katherine agreed unapologetically. Then she smiled at him. "But you realize what Jess means to you now and that's what matters."

"I hope she feels that way. I hope it's not too late." Brice raked his fingers through his hair. "I'm going to

L.A. to ask her to come back here so we can try to work something out. There's a flight out of here at two A.M., so I'll just stay at the casino tonight and one of the boys can drive me from there to the airport. Hopefully, I'll be back by tomorrow night, with Jess."

"I'm sure you will. Everything will work out, you'll see."

"We'll have a lot to talk about," Brice murmured. "I may have to be very persuasive."

"You're not planning to ask Jess to come back to things the same way they were, are you?" Katherine asked suspiciously. "You are going to ask her to marry you? I don't think she'll settle for anything less now."

"I don't think so, either." Her father smiled wryly. "I never imagined I'd get married again, but . . ." He shrugged. "Oh well, if Jess will marry me, I just hope I'm not a disappointment to her."

"She loves you, Daddy," Katherine reminded him softly. "She won't be disappointed."

Though Brice had rarely ever displayed his feelings for Katherine physically, he reached out now to gently ruffle her hair. "You're a good child, Kit," he said with a fond smile. "We have a lot of talking to do, too, but I hope you'll understand if Jess gets most of my attention in the next few weeks . . . if I can get her to come back with me."

Katherine nodded. "I'll understand."

As her father stood, his expression became very sober again. "Promise me something," he muttered abruptly, his green eyes icy as he stared over her at Jason who still stood at the water's edge. "Promise me you'll spend tonight at home."

Katherine blushed, looking around quickly at Jason, as if she feared he might have overheard what her father said. "I planned to stay home tonight," she said weakly at last. "I don't know what you're worried about."

"Yes, you do. Nobody knows much about Jason Roarke, Kit, so that means he's something of a loner. He'll probably always be and I hope you'll remember that. I'd hate to see you get hurt." After casting one last none-too-friendly look in Jason's direction, Brice turned and started to walk away. "See you tomorrow night. I hope."

Katherine couldn't even answer him. With those few words, he had renewed all her doubts about Jason and suddenly she knew what she had to do. She had to get away from here because her father was right. She would get hurt if she allowed herself to become any more involved with Jason than she already was.

Obviously noticing Brice's departure, Jason joined Katherine again, reaching down to take her hand to draw her to her feet. "How's the ankle?" he murmured, spanning her waist with large yet gentle hands. "Better?"

Unable to look up at him, she fixed her gaze on the pulse beating in his tan neck. "It's nearly well," she murmured, then before she could lose her nerve, blurted out, "I'm going home to Baltimore tomorrow."

Jason tensed. For a long moment, he said nothing. Then his hands around her waist exerted rough pressure as he pulled her closer to him. "Why?" he asked roughly. "Why are you leaving now?"

Haltingly, she explained about her father's plan to bring Jess back. "I-I just think they'll n-need time alone when they get back," she concluded. "I wouldn't want to get in their way."

"You're lying, Kit," he muttered harshly, grasping her small chin between his thumb and forefinger, tilting her head back so she had to face him. "You're just trying to get away from me. Are you *that* afraid of me?"

"Yes," she answered honestly, pain darkening her green eyes to pools of jade. "My father says you're a loner and I think he's right. You'll always have women like Julie in your life, but I . . . I couldn't be one of them."

"You're not going to give me a chance, are you?" he uttered furiously. "I'm a gambler, so I can't be dependable. Right? But how do you justify the fact that you want me? You can't tell me it means nothing when I touch you. Like this." Without warning, he lowered his head. His mouth took possession of hers as he gathered her closer. His lips closed on the soft curve of her lower lip and as her mouth opened slightly to his, his tongue tasted the sweetness within. His hands moved over her firm hips, into the inward curve of her narrow waist, then up to play over her breasts and he groaned softly in triumph when the tumescent nipples surged against his palms. As he lowered the straps of her white gauze sundress and his lips sought her bare shoulders, she melted against him, wrapping her slender arms around his neck. She wanted him, ached to know his complete possession and her parted lips clung to the firm warmth of his until he pulled away slightly.

"You see, Kit," he whispered, his warm minty breath fanning her hot cheeks, "we need each other."

His words brought her back to reality with a jolt. Tears filled her eyes. "But it's only physical need," she said thickly. "That's not enough for me."

His narrowed gaze held hers. "Physical need is a part of the relationship between a man and a woman, Kit. It's no sin."

"But if that's all there is . . ."

"Why are you so certain that's all there is between us?" he interrupted, almost impatiently. "Why are you so afraid to take a chance with me? Because I'm a gambler?

175

If so, that's a very shallow reason. Sure, you'll be taking a chance. And I'll be taking a chance with you. When a man and a woman get involved in a deep relationship, it's always a game of chance. It might work out and it might not. That's just the way life is. We all have to take risks. And if you don't know that, you're living in some little-girl dream world."

"Jason, I . . ." Katherine's words halted as he gripped her shoulders and shook her slightly. Auburn strands of silken hair fell across her paling cheeks and she gazed up at him with wide, startled eyes.

"Is this really the way you want it to end?" he asked roughly. "Is it, Kit?"

"No," she whispered. "But the ending I want is impossible."

Jason's hands dropped away from her. "If you'd only trusted me, Kit, I think we could have had something very special together."

"Yes, it would have been special," she muttered unhappily. "But how long would it have lasted?"

"Since you have to ask that question, it could never begin," he answered brusquely, then shook his head. "Don't wait until everything is perfect, Kit. That may never happen with any man. You'll have to take a chance or be alone the way Brice has been for years. But maybe you're more like him than you thought; maybe you're as afraid to make a commitment as he's always been, until now."

"No!" she gasped, her face white. "That's not true! I . . ."

"Good-bye, Kit," he interrupted softly, leaning down to brush a kiss across her forehead before he turned and walked away.

Katherine spun around to stare blindly at the lake, unable to watch him leave her. Tears filled her eyes, blurring her vision. An aching empty void spread within her and she felt cold inside. She felt as if he had ripped the very essence of her being from her and carried it away with him. She lifted icy fingers to press against icy cheeks but her unhappiness was too deep and devastating to find any release in tears.

Chapter Eleven

Katherine was driving to the airport the next morning when she changed her mind. All night and since she had gotten out of bed, she had been doubting the wisdom of her decision to leave Tahoe. But that old instinct for self preservation had driven her to pack, get in the car, and start for the airport. Now, as she moved farther and farther away from Jason, she knew she didn't want to leave him at all.

A sudden trembling overtook her and she pulled her father's Porsche off the road into the parking lot of one of the casinos near the state line. Gripping the steering wheel tightly, she rested her forehead against her hands, trying to take deep calming breaths. She was on the verge of making a momentous decision, one that could alter her entire life but, though she wanted to approach her problem logically, logic had little influence over her emotions.

Jason was the only man she would probably ever love. He was intelligent, exciting, and he had always been very gentle, almost loving, with her. She was stupid to even consider leaving him, she finally decided. Perhaps he was right—love was a game of chance. And if it was, she would rather take her chances with him than with any other man she had known or ever hoped to meet. Undoubtedly, if she tried, she could find more security with a man like Brad Whitney, but he had bored her to tears and suddenly security didn't seem all that important to her if she had to live with a dullard to achieve it. Even if Jason only wanted to be with her for a few months, he would give her more happiness than she would find in fifty years with a man like Brad. And, maybe, if she were really lucky, Jason might fall in love with her and never want to leave. The odds against that happening were astronomically high; she realized that. Jason was a gambler and gamblers rarely settled down, but even with the odds against her, she was ready to take the risk. Actually, she had little choice. Since Jason had walked away from her at the lake last night, she had felt empty and alone. Now, she knew she would be an idiot to leave the only man who could make her feel alive.

Katherine raised her head. Excitement and determination sparkled in her eyes. She was going back to Jason. Mallie would be horrified and Brice would probably have fits, but Katherine couldn't really care. This was her life, her risk. Turning the car around in the parking lot, she headed back the way she had come. She had planned to leave her father's Porsche at the airport for him to pick up on his return from L.A. so she made a mental note to be certain someone was there to meet his plane.

Now that she had made the decision to go to Jason, she could hardly wait to get to his house . . . until she actually turned off the road onto his driveway. Then all sorts of unjustified fears assaulted her. What if he had changed his mind about wanting her? He had been upset with her last night. What if he rejected her today? She didn't think she could bear that since she had battled and defeated all her strongest inhibitions to decide to come to him in the first place.

To Katherine's relief, Jason's Jaguar was parked in his drive but there was a strange car parked there also and she prayed it didn't belong to Julie. She had no idea what she could say to Jason if that blond bombshell were there or if, indeed, he would give her a chance to say anything at all. Yet, she knew she had to try. Before her courage could desert her, she parked the Porsche, got out, and removed the jacket of her grass-green suit and tossed it back onto the front seat of the car. Squaring her shoulders, she walked briskly toward the house, sighing audibly with relief when a man came out the front door just as she reached it. Dressed sportily in a navy blazer and white slacks, he carried a briefcase and wore a pleasant smile on his fortyish face. He was a stranger, but Katherine smiled back at him almost gratefully. Obviously the strange car belonged to him, so Julie wasn't inside with Jason as she had feared.

After the man held the front door open for Katherine, she murmured her thanks politely, then stepped into the cedar-paneled foyer, forgetting completely that she hadn't knocked. Her heart was thudding so violently she had difficulty breathing and she had the distinct impression that her knees would knock if she gave them half a chance. So she didn't. Immediately, she stepped into the great room, then stopped as she saw Jason. His back to her, he was standing at a side window looking out at the trees. His hands were thrust into the pockets of his tobacco-brown trousers and the cream-colored polo shirt accentuated his tanned skin. She watched as he massaged the back of his neck with one lean hand. After having come all this way, at least emotionally, she now found she couldn't take the remaining few steps between them. But Jason saved her from having to. As if he sensed her presence, he turned around slowly, but Katherine couldn't tell if the sudden light that flared in his eyes denoted anger or a welcome. His expression was remote; he simply stared at her, creating such overwhelming tension in her she thought she would explode. When he moved abruptly toward her, her heart lurched and she took a step backward, trapping herself against the newel post at the foot of the stairs. Jason stopped close in front of her and her eyes dilated and widened as she gulped and gazed up at him.

"Well, Kit," he murmured emotionlessly. "Have you come to say good-bye?"

Though she longed to throw herself into his arms, she didn't dare. If he rejected her, she wanted to retain at least the tattered remnants of her pride. Her throat was too dry for her to speak and the tip of her tongue came out to moisten her lips. His jaw tightened as he waited a long, tense moment for her answer and at last she shook her head.

"Then why are you here?" he persisted softly. But, amazingly, he cupped her face in both his hands. "Tell me."

Katherine closed her eyes, his touch warming her entire body with an odd sense of belonging and security. Her own hands sought his hard chest, her fingers stroking the knit fabric of his shirt as her eyes opened slowly again to meet the compelling light in his. "I can't go, Jason," she whispered. "I don't want to leave you, no matter . . ."

"*Kit*," he murmured, his mouth descending swiftly to cover hers, halting her words with a gentle yet seeking kiss. His hands moved urgently down over her back to her waist, arching her to him as her arms encircled his neck and she raised up on tiptoe, inviting a rougher taking of her mouth. His lips released hers, however, to blaze a burning trail along her creamy throat to the hollow beneath her ear. "Thank God you didn't go," he groaned, his deep voice muffled in the thickness of her hair.

Relief washed over her, weakening her limbs. She felt dizzy with happiness as she leaned back against his arms to look up at him. "I love you," she said huskily. "You may not want to hear that but I do."

"Not want to hear it?" he exclaimed softly, his eyes narrowing to slits. "I never wanted to hear anything more in my life. Kit, I love you, too."

Chewing her lip, she shook her head. "You don't have to say that. Really. I'll stay with you anyway, as long as you want me."

His short laugh combined with a groan. "Little idiot," he uttered hoarsely, then took her mouth again hungrily with only a slight hint of tenderness as her lips parted eagerly at the first touch of his. As his hands explored her soft curves, their kiss slowly altered from its initial urgency to a languorous sharing of sensuous delight. Accepting total surrender as inevitable, Katherine moved against him, pliant and acquiescent in his arms, but as Jason obviously realized she no longer controlled her responses, he dragged his mouth from hers reluctantly, his breathing ragged. Hard fingers kneaded her waist and he smiled gently as she gazed up at him with drowsy eyes. "Kit, you crazy child, I do love you. And where did you get the idea I just wanted you to live with me for a while? That's not exactly the kind of commitment I wanted you to make."

"You don't want me to live with you?" she questioned bewilderedly. "But what . . ."

"I want you to *live* with me—but as my wife," he interrupted, placing a kiss on the tip of her small nose as she gasped. "How could you believe I'd ask an innocent like you to just move in with me. You're the kind of young woman a man wants to marry, Kit. And I want you to marry me. Very soon."

Katherine actually felt faint. Her mouth nearly fell open as she stared up at him with wide incredulous eyes.

Gamblers didn't propose marriage! But this one just had and after it finally dawned on her that he really meant it, she propelled herself closer to him, laughing tearfully as his strong arms tightened around her and he lifted her off her feet. "I've been so miserable," she whispered. "Why didn't you tell me all this before?"

"You wouldn't have believed me. I'm surprised you believe me now."

"Maybe I do because I want to so much," she murmured against his neck. "Or maybe I'm beginning to trust you."

Holding her away from him, Jason searched her face. "Are you sure you can trust a gambler?"

"I think I can trust *you*. No matter what you are."

"I was beginning to think I'd never hear you say that," he answered huskily, tracing the bow-shaped outline of her mouth with one fingertip. Yet, when her lips parted with the caress, he didn't kiss her. "Kit, I have something to tell you." He hesitated a moment before continuing, "As you came in today, did you see a man leaving?" When she nodded, he smiled almost sheepishly. "Well, that was Bill Anders, my editor from New York. He's on his way to San Francisco so he stopped here to see me."

"Editor," Katherine squeaked, understanding immediately what Jason was saying yet not really able to believe it. "You're not saying you're . . . You can't be *that* Jason Roarke! Not the writer!"

Saying nothing, Jason nodded.

"But you can't be!" she persisted, thoroughly confused. "You're a gambler. You have to be! You always win."

"No, I don't, Kit," he replied softly, massaging her tensed shoulders. "Nobody who gambles wins all the time."

"But how could you *ever* win, if you're not a professional gambler?" Katherine argued, unable to accept what he was saying. "Not many people could just sit down with professional gamblers and ever win even one game. So how did you do it?"

"I've played poker for years," Jason explained. "And I spent three months with an old pro who taught me everything he knew about the finer points of poker. With that and a lot of luck, I managed to get by."

"But why should you want to?" she protested. As she scanned his face for some indication that he was lying and found none, she shook her head bewilderedly. "I just don't understand."

"It was research, Kit. Professional gamblers have always intrigued me, but to write about one, I needed to become one for a while, to experience exactly the kind of life they live."

"You deliberately deceived me then!" Katherine accused, her eyes flashing green fire as she tried to pull away from him. But when his hold on her only tightened, her struggling ceased though she glared up at him resentfully. "Why? Why did you have to lie to me? You even told me your ex-wife disapproved of your gambling."

Jason shook his head. "No, I didn't, Kit. I distinctly remember telling you she disapproved of my *profession*, which she did. When Denise and I got married, I was a struggling short-story writer, selling very few, and she thought and often said I should stop wasting my time on such nonsense and go out and find a real job."

"But letting me *assume* she disapproved of your gambling was just as bad as telling an outright lie," Katherine muttered bitterly. "Why couldn't you just tell me the truth? I wouldn't have had to drive myself crazy trying not to love you if I'd known you weren't a gambler."

"Some people think writing for a living is as irresponsible and risky as gambling," Jason said wryly, trailing his fingers along her slender neck. Then his expression sobered again. "Denise believed that and after my experience with her, Kit, it was important to me for you to love me and trust me because of who I am, not what I do."

"Oh." Katherine bent her head, all her resentment draining away abruptly, leaving her feeling very ashamed of herself. "You were testing me. And I almost failed the test. Jason, I nearly left this morning. I was on my way to the airport."

"But you didn't get there," he reminded her, smiling indulgently, his thumbs brushing caressingly over her high cheekbones. "And the fact that you decided not to leave is all that matters now."

"No, there's one more thing I need to know," Katherine murmured. "If . . . if I had gone this morning, would you . . . have just let it all end that way?"

Jason laughed softly. "No. I have a feeling I would have manufactured some excuse to visit Baltimore very soon. I didn't want to lose you, Kit."

"You never will now," she promised, content with his answer. Lifting her arms up around his shoulders, she pressed her cheek against his chest. "I love you, Jason. So very much."

"Does that mean you're accepting my marriage proposal?" he inquired unnecessarily, a note of loving amusement in his voice. "Are you saying yes, Kit?"

"Yes," she whispered, her breath catching as he gathered her closer, his mouth taking hers with tender, irresistible passion. For a long time the silence in the room was broken only by the intimate endearments he whispered against her lips. Then, at last, when their desire for each other threatened to burn out of control, he put her from him, his eyes glittering sapphires as he held her gaze. "If I asked you to stay here with me until we can get married, would you, Kit?" he asked huskily. "Could you trust me that much?"

"Yes," Katherine answered without hesitation. "I never want to leave you, even for a minute."

"I'm glad to hear it," he replied with a teasing smile. "But I won't make you prove your newfound faith in me. This is Nevada. Remember? The land of the quickie divorce and, luckily for us, the even quicker marriage. So, we won't even have to rush around madly to be married by this evening. Or is today too soon for you?"

Enchanting rose color tinted Katherine's cheeks but she answered truthfully "I'm not sure I can even wait until this evening."

"Ummm, I like your attitude," Jason murmured, tangling his fingers in her hair as he smiled down at her. "If you're that eager to be my wife, then we should have a fascinating honeymoon and a very long, happy marriage." Brushing her hair back over her shoulder, he lowered his head to nibble the tender lobe of her ear. "And I won't be gambling anymore, Kit. If we really try, I'm certain we can think of more exciting ways to spend our nights. Don't you?"

We'll think of something to do, I'm sure," she answered, laughing softly up at him until his gently marauding mouth covered hers and altered her laughter to a breathless whispering of his name.

Silhouette ❦ *Romance*

15-Day Free Trial Offer
6 Silhouette Romances

6 Silhouette Romances, free for 15 days! We'll send you 6 new Silhouette Romances to keep for 15 days, absolutely free! If you decide not to keep them, send them back to us. You pay nothing.

Free Home Delivery. But if you enjoy them as much as we think you will, keep them by paying the invoice enclosed with your free trial shipment. We'll pay all shipping and handling charges. You get the convenience of Home Delivery and we pay the postage and handling charge each month.

Don't miss a copy. The Silhouette Book Club is the way to make sure you'll be able to receive every new romance we publish before they're sold out. There is no minimum number of books to buy and you can cancel at any time.

Silhouette Romance

IT'S YOUR OWN SPECIAL TIME

Contemporary romances for today's women.
Each month, six very special love stories will be yours
from SILHOUETTE. Look for them wherever books are sold
or order now from the coupon below.

$1.50 each

Hampson	☐ 1 ☐ 4 ☐ 16 ☐ 27 ☐ 28 ☐ 40 ☐ 52 ☐ 64 ☐ 94	Browning	☐ 12 ☐ 38 ☐ 53 ☐ 73 ☐ 93
Stanford	☐ 6 ☐ 25 ☐ 35 ☐ 46 ☐ 58 ☐ 88	Michaels	☐ 15 ☐ 32 ☐ 61 ☐ 87
		John	☐ 17 ☐ 34 ☐ 57 ☐ 85
Hastings	☐ 13 ☐ 26 ☐ 44 ☐ 67	Beckman	☐ 8 ☐ 37 ☐ 54 ☐ 72 ☐ 96
Vitek	☐ 33 ☐ 47 ☐ 66 ☐ 84		

$1.50 each

☐ 5 Goforth	☐ 29 Wildman	☐ 56 Trent	☐ 79 Halldorson
☐ 7 Lewis	☐ 30 Dixon	☐ 59 Vernon	☐ 80 Stephens
☐ 9 Wilson	☐ 31 Halldorson	☐ 60 Hill	☐ 81 Roberts
☐ 10 Caine	☐ 36 McKay	☐ 62 Hallston	☐ 82 Dailey
☐ 11 Vernon	☐ 39 Sinclair	☐ 63 Brent	☐ 83 Halston
☐ 14 Oliver	☐ 41 Owen	☐ 69 St. George	☐ 86 Adams
☐ 19 Thornton	☐ 42 Powers	☐ 70 Afton Bonds	☐ 89 James
☐ 20 Fulford	☐ 43 Robb	☐ 71 Ripy	☐ 90 Major
☐ 21 Richards	☐ 45 Carroll	☐ 74 Trent	☐ 92 McKay
☐ 22 Stephens	☐ 48 Wildman	☐ 75 Carroll	☐ 95 Wisdom
☐ 23 Edwards	☐ 49 Wisdom	☐ 76 Hardy	☐ 97 Clay
☐ 24 Healy	☐ 50 Scott	☐ 77 Cork	☐ 98 St. George
	☐ 55 Ladame	☐ 78 Oliver	☐ 99 Camp

$1.75 each

☐ 100 Stanford	☐ 105 Eden	☐ 110 Trent	☐ 115 John
☐ 101 Hardy	☐ 106 Dailey	☐ 111 South	☐ 116 Lindley
☐ 102 Hastings	☐ 107 Bright	☐ 112 Stanford	☐ 117 Scott
☐ 103 Cork	☐ 108 Hampson	☐ 113 Browning	☐ 118 Dailey
☐ 104 Vitek	☐ 109 Vernon	☐ 114 Michaels	☐ 119 Hampson

Silhouette Romance

Coming next month from
Silhouette Romances

Strangers May Marry by Anne Hampson

Only Paul could help Laura keep her adopted child, but in return he demanded marriage! Was his price too high, or could Laura find true happiness married to a stranger?

Run From Heartache by Brenda Trent

Summer had lost her memory in the accident that brought Bracken into her life. But the past could never diminish her desire to share the future with this loving man.

One Man Forever by Juliet Ashby

Winging her way toward Paris with her new boss, Penny wondered if she could handle the job, and more importantly, could she handle the autocratic and devastating Pierce Reynolds?

Search For Love by Nora Roberts

He was suspicious, jealous, demanding and impossible! So why in heaven's name had Serenity lost her heart to her French cousin, Christophe, Count de Kergallen?

Island On The Hill by Dixie Browning

Frances had worked hard for her independence, and she wasn't about to give it up for a man. But rugged, handsome Cabel was more than a man—he was a lover!

Arranged Marriage by Brittany Young

Analisa had married Rafael Santiago out of respect for her dying father. But she hadn't anticipated the scorching flame of his love under the reddening Spanish sun.

READERS' COMMENTS ON SILHOUETTE ROMANCES:

"I would like to congratulate you on the most wonderful books I've had the pleasure of reading. They are a tremendous joy to those of us who have yet to meet the man of our dreams. From reading your books I quite truly believe that he will someday appear before me like a prince!"
—L.L.*, Hollandale, MS

"Your books are great, wholesome fiction, always with an upbeat, happy ending. Thank you."
—M.D., Massena, NY

"My boyfriend always teases me about Silhouette Books. He asks me, how's my love life and naturally I say terrific, but I tell him that there is always room for a little more romance from Silhouette."
—F.N., Ontario, Canada

"I would like to sincerely express my gratitude to you and your staff for bringing the pleasure of your publications to my attention. Your books are well written, mature and very contemporary."
—D.D., Staten Island, NY

*names available on request